Steidl
Spring/Summer 2018

SOUVENIRS
of
My Inky Past

Remarks by Carl Purington Rollins
at the opening of an exhibition of his
printing at the Grolier Club
April 19, 1949

New York
The New York Public Library
1950

Souvenirs of My Inky Past

*Remarks by Carl Purington Rollins at the opening
of the exhibition of his printing at the Grolier
Club on the evening of April 19, 1949*

IT is one of the more felicitous privileges of the bookman's life to meet in this hall. In the sixty-odd years of the Grolier Club's existence, it has made a distinguished name for itself as an association of book collectors and book makers. And I think it is sometimes overlooked that without book makers, that is to say, without the artisans who print and bind books, there would be no book dealers, book collectors, or book guardians — that is, librarians.*

Amongst the founders of this Club were several men directly concerned with printing and book production: Robert Hoe, the maker of printing presses; Theodore Low DeVinne, the most learned printer whom America has produced; Arthur Turnure, who has recently been called "the aesthetic printer"; and others intimately concerned with the publication of books. To print and publish books of superior physical appearance was one of the primary aims of the

* It is in this capacity that the Library asked Mr. Rollins for permission to publish these "remarks." Our thanks go to him and to Frederick B. Adams, Jr., President of the Grolier Club, for their gracious agreement that the *Bulletin* would be a suitable place for the permanent record. — EDITOR.

Club, and one which it has consistently adhered to. In the early days DeVinne gave several lectures on types and printing, lectures later issued in printed form. And finally the Club early set out to amass a collection of books on the subject which our German friends have rather aptly called "the book arts." These bibliographical and typographical treasures now constitute one of the most important collections of such books which we have. You will find there a copy of *Mechanick Exercises or the Doctrine of Handy-Works Applied to the Art of Printing*, written by Joseph Moxon and published at London in 1683, the first English manual of the printer's craft, of very great importance historically. Beside it there is the notable two-volume reprint made in 1896 by Theodore DeVinne as a fitting testimonial to Joseph Moxon and the practice of printing. It was DeVinne and the Grolier Club which first in this country emphasized the "mechanick exercise" of printing and book making as of equal importance, at least, with the sentimental lore of book loving.

Even the most devoted printer must acknowledge that he must have a text to print, though I have known customers who seemed to labor under the delusion that the printing could begin before the copy was ready! But manners must adorn knowledge, and it is the printer's province

to take the raw material of the book, the text, and give it comely form. It has not infrequently happened that the printer tends to mistake his calling, and attempts a primary object of artistic creation, confusing the means for the end. It was probably a fit of exasperation at the *édition de grande luxe* which caused Mrs. Warde to write that "type must be invisible." The American wood engraver, William J. Linton, had a theory that black ink was offensive to the eye, and his books, printed at his Appledore private press, were printed in so faint a color that they are almost unreadable for the average person. There can be no stranger contrast than that between his books and those of Morris at the Kelmscott Press! Some readers find these latter books over-emphatic in manner.

The printing press, by its very name, implies that the type is to be impressed into the paper, and by that means rendered readable and permanent. For it is the permanence of print which is one of its great contributions to human development. Permanence, of course, is a relative term, when applied to the handiworks of man, and five hundred years, the life span of the oldest printing, is a short period as compared with the Spanish cave paintings or the Rosetta stone. Other human records, such as the prehistoric "shredded wheat biscuit," as my friend George

Day calls the baked clay tablets of Babylon, have a far longer history. But no one knows how long the printed records may yet live to be. Certainly the vellum incunabula can have no predictable time of degeneration and decay. And the great Gutenberg Bible shows no evidence of mortality. Look at its black ink, probably still soft under its hard surface, and, since the eye alone is not sufficient, feel of its strong, tough linen paper, and predict if you dare that Macaulay's traveler from New Zealand may not find it still as vigorous as ever under the rubble of the British Museum. Even the trash of the wood pulp era, imprisoned between walls of silk, may have a life expectancy beyond our guessing.

Compared with other modern means of recording thought, printing is indeed perdurable. The radio broadcast you heard this morning has gone with the wind. Even if recorded on a phonograph record, that may be broken into a thousand pieces by an inadvertent blow. The popular wire recording can be expunged with a magnet. But even if we grant that some methods of modern recording may be permanent, printing still has one advantage over any other known method — that it can make invariant copies immediately available quickly and cheaply. Mr. William M. Ivins pointed out, in a brilliant lecture a year ago, that a neglected aspect of printing is that it

provided, for the first time in human history, a means of making invariant copies. His interest was, of course, in the printing of pictures, but the same argument holds true of letter-press printing from type. Here the bibliographer will cry "Hold! What of variant copies?" It is true that in the operation of the hand press changes can be made on work in process; even so, there will be many copies printed before and after such changes, and save to the specialist and the diligent seeker who wants to know "more and more about less and less," it is true that the printed book is a matter of multiple invariant copies. The King James version of the Bible exists in thousands of copies which, so far as actual words are concerned, vary not at all from each other. But where do we find one codex of a text which is precisely like another?

Fond of our archaic cast lead type, accustomed to our uncouth roman letters, preferring the solid, penetrating impression into the surface of paper made from linen rags, I am by no means sure that these elements of printing are sure to last. Chinese and Arabic symbols are much handsomer than even Jenson's or Bodoni's or Caslon's or Bruce Rogers' type forms. The energetic protagonists of the manuscript hand suggest a new calligraphy. The camera, which was the key to the ubiquitous and loathsome half-tone print-

ing block, has now been harnessed to the composing machine. And finally Senefelder's method of surface printing, developed into the offset press, permits of a much greater flexibility than the printing press. It may well be that before the six-hundredth anniversary of Gutenberg's invention rolls around, the whole process of printing will be changed. The devoted apostles of electronics may even eliminate printer's ink, and the plasticists, paper! But so far as one may see at the moment, printing will still provide us with the readiest, cheapest, most useful and most permanent way of recording human thought.

Index

Contents

Steidl

Düstere Str. 4
37073 Göttingen
Germany
T +49 551 4 960 60
F +49 551 4 960 649
E mail@steidl.de
www.steidl.de

Sales

Matthias Wegener
T +49 551 4 960 616
F +49 551 4 960 649
E mwegener@steidl.de

Susanne Schmidt
T +49 551 4 960 612
F +49 551 4 960 649
E sschmidt@steidl.de

Submissions

Holger Feroudj
E holger@steidl.de

Catalogue / Editorial

Holger Feroudj
T +49 551 49060 621
E holger@steidl.de

Export Management / Shipping

Jan Menkens
T +49 551 4 960 618
F +49 551 4 960 617
E jmenkens@steidl.de

Production

Bernard Fischer
T +49 551 4 960 633
F +49 551 4 960 634
E bfischer@steidl.de

Public Relations / Press

Claudia Glenewinkel
T +49 551 4 960 650
F +49 551 4 960 644
E cglenewinkel@steidl.de

Germany, Austria and Switzerland

Steidl Verlag
Claudia Glenewinkel
Düstere Str. 4
37073 Göttingen
Germany
T +49 551 4 960 650
F +49 551 4 960 644
E presse@steidl.de

USA and Canada

Monika Condrea
39 Ainslie Street
Brooklyn, NY 11211
USA
T +1 646 226 6828
E monika.condrea@gmail.com

France

Patrick Remy
22, Place Charles Fillion
75017 Paris
France
T +33 1 42 632 167
F +33 1 42 265 518
E patremy2@wanadoo.fr

All other territories

Steidl Verlag
Claudia Glenewinkel
Düstere Str. 4
37073 Göttingen
Germany
T +49 551 4 960 650
F +49 551 4 960 644
E presse@steidl.de

Edition 7L Paris

Caroline Lebar
7, rue de Lille
75007 Paris
France
T +33 1 44 502 200
F +33 1 44 502 205
E caroline.lebar@karllagerfeld.com

Steidl Dangin Publishers

Box Ltd.
Attn.: Marion Liang
267 Douglass Street
Brooklyn, NY 11217
USA
T +1 212 965 9555
F +1 212 965 9555
E info@boxstudios.com

Steidl David Zwirner

Julia Joern
525 West 19th Street
New York, NY 10011
T +1 212 7 272 070
F +1 212 7 272 072
E julia@davidzwirner.com
www.davidzwirner.com

Steidl Miles

Peter Miles Studio
650 East 6th Street, Apt. 1
New York, NY 10009
T +1 212 3 587 991
E email@petermilesstudio.com

Verlag

Gerhard Steidl
GmbH & Co. OHG
Düstere Straße 4
37073 Göttingen
T +49 551 4 960 60
F +49 551 4 960 649
E mail@steidl.de
www.steidl.de

Vertrieb

Matthias Wegener
T +49 551 4 960 616
F +49 551 4 960 649
E mwegener@steidl.de

Susanne Schmidt
T +49 551 4 960 612
F +49 551 4 960 649
E sschmidt@steidl.de

Auslieferungen

Deutschland

Gemeinsame Verlagsauslieferung
Göttingen (GVA)
Postfach 2021
37010 Göttingen
T +49 551 487 177
F +49 551 41 392
E bestellung@gva-verlage.de

Lieferanschrift:
Anna-Vandenhoeck-Ring 36
37081 Göttingen

Auftragsbearbeitung:
Leonore Frester
T +49 551 487 177
F +49 551 41 392
E frester@gva-verlage.de

Lisa Jacobi
T +49 551 487 177
F +49 551 41 392
E jakobi@gva-verlage.de

Österreich

Mohr-Morawa
Sulzengasse 2
A-1232 Wien
T +43 1 680 140
F +43 1 687 130
E bestellung@mohrmorawa.at

Schweiz

AVA
Centralweg 16
CH-8910 Affoltern am Albis
T +41 44 7 624 200
F +41 44 7 624 210
E avainfo@ava.ch

Außendienst

Deutschland

Schleswig-Holstein, Hamburg, Bremen, Niedersachsen

Bodo Föhr Verlagsvertretungen
Lattenkamp 90
22299 Hamburg
T +49 40 51493667
F +49 40 51493666
E bodofoehr@freenet.de

Berlin, Mecklenburg-Vorpommern, Brandenburg

Vera Grambow
Liselotte-Herrmann-Straße 2
10407 Berlin
T +49 30 40 048 583
F +49 30 4 212 246
E berliner-verlagsvertretungen
  @t-online.de

Sachsen-Anhalt, Sachsen, Thüringen

Thomas Kilian
Vor dem Riedtor 11
99310 Arnstadt
T +49 362 85 493 310
F +49 362 85 493 310
E thomas.c.kilian@web.de

Nordrhein-Westfalen

Benedikt Geulen
Meertal 122
41464 Neuss
T +49 2131 1 255 990
F +49 2131 1 257 944
E benedikt.geulen@t-online.de

Ulrike Hölzemann
Dornseiferstr.67
57223 Kreuztal
T +49 2732 55 83 44
F +49 2732 55 83 45
E u.hoelzemann@buerofuerbuecher.de

Hessen, Rheinland-Pfalz, Saarland, Luxemburg

Raphael Pfaff
Verlagsvetretung
An den Drei Hohen 51
60435 Frankfurt
T +49 69 54 890 366
F +49 69 549 024
E raphael.pfaff@web.de

Baden-Württemberg

Tilmann Eberhardt
Verlagsvertretungen
Ludwigstr. 93
70197 Stuttgart
T +49 711 615 28 20
F +49 711 615 31 01
E Tilmann.Eberhardt@gmail.com

Bayern

Günter Schubert
Brunnenstraße 20a
85598 Baldham
T +49 8106 377 23 97
F +49 8106 377 23 98
E guenterschubert@t-online.de

Österreich

Jürgen Sieberer
Arnikaweg 79/4
1220 Wien
T +43 285 45 22
F +43 285 45 22
E juergen.sieberer@mohrmorawa.at

Günter Thiel
Reuharting 11
4652 Steinerkirchen
T +43 664 3 912 835
F +43 664 773 912 835
E guenter.thiel@mohrmorawa.at

Schweiz

Giovanni Ravasio
Verlagsvertretungen
Klosbachstr. 33
CH-8032 Zürich
T +41 44 260 61 31
F +41 44 260 61 32
E g.ravasio@bluewin.ch

Artbook | D.A.P.

75 Broad Street
Suite 630
New York, N.Y. 10004
USA
T +1 212 627 1999
F +1 212 627 9484
E orders@dapinc.com
www.artbook.com

Trade Sales Representatives

USA — West Coast / Southwest

Ellen Towell
Karel/Dutton Group
3145 Geary Blvd. #619
San Francisco CA 94118
T +1 415-668-0829
F +1 415-668-2463
E hkarel@comcast.net

Lise Solomon
Albany CA
T +1 510-528-0579
F +1 510-900-1088
E lise.solomon@sonic.net

Dory Dutton
Karel/Dutton Group
Corrales NM
T +1 818-269-4882
F +1 480-247-5158
E dory.dutton
   @valleyvillageemail.com

Bob Harrison
Seattle WA
T +1 206-542-1545
F +1 206-546-5716
E bharrison451@earthlink.net

Southern California

Tricia Gabriel
T +1 323-969-8985
F +1 323-662-7896
E tgabriel@dapinc.com

Midwest

Stu Abraham
Minneapolis MN
T +1 952-927-7920
F +1 952-927-8089
E stu@aabookreps.com

John Mesjak
Sycamore IL 60178
T +1 815-899-0079
F +1 815-261-4114
E john@aabookreps.com

Roy Schonfeld
South Euclid OH
T +1 216-291-3538
F +1 216-691-0548
E roy@aabookreps.com

Emily Johnson
St. Paul MN
T +1 952 927 7920
F +1 952 927 8089
E emily@aabookreps.com

Mid-South / Southeast

Bill McClung / Terri McClung
Spring Branch TX
T +1 888-813-6563
F +1 888-311-8932
E bmcclung@ix.netcom.com
E tmcclung@ix.netcom.com

New England / Southeast

Jane Brown
T +1 323-969-8985
F +1 818-243-4676
E mcbooks@aol.com

Mark Pearson
CT, RI, MA, NH, VT, ME,
VA, NC, SC, GA, FL
T 617-480-1709
F 800-478-3128
E mpearson@dapinc.com

Mid-Atlantic

Chesapeake & Hudson, Inc.
Michael Gourley, Bill Hoar, Janine
Jensen, Steve Straw, Ted Wedel
T +1 800-231-4469
F +1 800-307-5163
E office@cheshud.com

National Accounts

Artbook | D.A.P.
Jane Brown
Los Angeles CA
T +1 323-969-8985
F +1 818-243-4676
E jbrown@dapinc.com

Gift Reps

Aesthetic Movement
New York & Mid-Atlantic
Gus Anagnopoulos
T +1 718-797-5750
F +1 718-797-4944
E gus@aestheticmovement.com

Aesthetic Movement
Chicago & Midwest
Alison Grant
T +1 773-951-8754
F +1 773-435-6691
E ali@aestheticmovement.com

Aesthetic Movement
Atlanta & Southern States
Laura Jane Turner
T +1 404-749-5005
F +1 404-521-4372
E laura@aestheticmovement.com

Artbook | Gift
Los Angeles & West Coast
Tricia Gabriel
T +1 323-969-8985
F +1 323-662-7896
E triciagabriel@gmail.com

Canada

Ampersand Inc.
Toronto On & East Coast
Saffron Beckwith
T +1 416-703-0666
F +1 866-849-3819
E saffronb@ampersandinc.ca

Ampersand Inc.
Vancouver BC & West Coast
Ali Hewitt
T +1 604-448-7165
F +1 888-323-7118
E cherylf@ampersandinc.ca

Ampersand Inc.
Ottawa & Quebec
Jenny Enriquez
T +1 416-703-0666
F +1 866-849-3819
E jennye@ampersandinc.ca

Paris Sales Office

Patrick Remy
22, Place Charles Fillion
75017 Paris
France
T +33 1 42 632 167
F +33 1 42 265 518
E patremy2@wanadoo.fr

For publications in English:

Interart S.A.R.L.
1, rue de l'Est
75020 Paris
T +33 1 43 493 660
F +33 1 43 494 122
E info@interart.fr

Responsable distribution:
Laurence H'Limi
E laurence@interart.fr

Responsable diffusion:
Pierre Samoyault
E pierre@interart.fr

Représentants:
Blanche Pilven
E blanche@interart.fr

Emerick Charpentier
E emerick@interart.fr

Margot Rietsch
E margot@interart.fr

Assistante commerciale:
Marylaure Perre
E marylaure@interart.fr

Service commande:
E commercial@interart.fr
www.dilicom.net

For publications in French:

SODIS
128, avenue du Maréchal-de-Lattre-
de-Tassigny
BP 142
77400 Lagny

Traitement des commandes
Responsable: Maeva Knisy
T +33 1 60 079 554

Identification DILICOM transmission:
SODILA (les commandes codifiées trans-
mises par DILICOM sont assurées du
traitement le plus rapide)
T +33 1 60 0 78 299
F +33 1 64 303 227

Relations clientèle
Chef de service: Pierrette Kimmel
T +33 1 60 078 201
F +33 1 64 308 805
E pierrette.kimmel@sodis.fr

Assistante Réclamations: Vic Mojasevic
T +33 1 60 078 633
F +33 1 64 308 806
E slavica.mojasevic@sodis.fr

Head Office / Export Sales Department: Thames & Hudson Ltd.

181a High Holborn
London WC1V 7QX
T +44 20 78 455 000
F +44 20 78 455 050
Sales and Marketing Department:
F +44 20 78 455 055
E sales@thameshudson.co.uk
E export@thameshudson.co.uk

UK Sales Office

Christian Frederking
Group Sales Director
T +44 20 7845 5000
F +44 20 7845 5055
E c.frederking@thameshudson.co.uk

Andrew Stanley
Deputy Head of Group Sales /
Head of UK Sales
T +44 20 7845 5000
F +44 20 7845 5055
E a.stanleyl@thameshudson.co.uk

Andrius Juknys
Head of Distributed books
T +44 20 7845 5000
F +44 20 7845 5055
E a.juknys@thameshudson.co.uk

Mark Garland
Manager, Distributed Books
T +44 20 7845 5000
F +44 20 7845 5055
E m.garland@thameshudson.co.uk

Jessica Arvidsson
Distributed Sales Co-ordinator
T +44 20 7845 5000
F +44 20 7845 5055
E j.arvidsson@thameshudson.co.uk

UK Territory Managers

Gethyn Jordan
Key Accounts Manager
National Wholesalers
T +44 20 7845 5000
F +44 20 7845 5055
E g.jordan@thameshudson.co.uk

Michelle Strickland
Key Accounts Manager
T +44 20 7845 5000
F +44 20 7845 5055
E m.strickland@thameshudson.co.uk

David Howson
Key Accounts and London
T +44 20 7845 5000
F +44 20 7845 5055
E d.howson@thameshudson.co.uk
London: E1-E18, EC1-4, N1-22, SE1, SW3,
SW7, W1, W2, W8, W11, WC2

Trade: Thames & Hudson (Distributors) Ltd. (distribution and accounts)

Littlehampton Book Services
Faraday Close
Durrington, Worthing
West Sussex BN13 3RB
United Kingdom
T +44 190 382 8501

Dawn Shield
Key Accounts and London
T +44 207 845 5000
F +44 207 845 5055
E d.shield@thameshudson.co.uk
London: NW1-NW11

Leslie Bolt
T +44 7984 034496
E l.bolt@thameshudson.co.uk
Bedfordshire, Berkshire, Cambridgeshire,
Dorset, Essex, Hampshire, Hertfordshire,
Kent, Middlesex, Norfolk, Suffolk, Surrey,
East Sussex, West Sussex, Wiltshire,
Worcestershire, Oxford, London SW4-6,
SW8-20, SE2-26, W3-7, W9-14

Karim White
T +44 7740 768900
E k.white@thameshudson.co.uk
Cheshire, Cleveland, Cumbria, Co.
Durham, Lancashire, Greater Manchester,
Merseyside, Northumberland, Sheffield,
Tyne & Wear, Yorkshire, Ireland, Scotland

Mike Lapworth
T +44 7745 304 088
E mikelapworth@sky.com
Buckinghamshire, Derbyshire, Hereford-
shire, Leicestershire, Lincolnshire, North-
ants, Nottinghamshire, Oxon (except
Oxford), Shropshire, Staffordshire, War-
wickshire, West Midlands, Worcestershire

Ian Tripp
T +44 7970 450162
E iantripp@ymail.com
Channel Islands Cornwall, Devon,
Gloucestershire, Somerset, Wales

Victoria Hutton
T +44 7899 941010
E victoriahuttonbooks@yahoo.co.uk
London Gift Accounts

James Denton
T +44 7765 403182
E jamesdenton778@btinternet.com
South and South East Gift Accounts

Central and South America, Mexico and The Carribean

Natasha Ffrench
Export Sales Department
Thames & Hudson Ltd
E n.ffrench@thameshudson.co.uk

Americas

Central & South America, Mexico and
The Caribbean
Natasha Ffrench
Export Sales Department
Thames & Hudson Ltd
E: n.ffrench@thameshudson.co.uk

Austria, Germany and Switzerland

Michael Klein
c/o Vertreterbuero Wuerzburg
T +49 931 17 405
F +49 931 17 410
E mi-klein@t-online.de

Austria, Germany and Switzerland

Michael Klein
c/o Vertreterbuero Wuerzburg
T. 0049 931 17 405
E: mi-klein@t-online.de

Belgium, Netherlands and Luxembourg

Bas van der Zee
T: + 31 (0) 623137695
E: b.vanderzee@thameshudson.co.uk

Eastern Europe

Sara Ticci
T: + 44 7952 919866
E: s.ticci@thameshudson.co.uk

Eastern Mediterranean, Bulgaria, Romania

Stephen Embrey
T: + 44 7952 919866
E: s.embrey@thameshudson.co.uk

France

Interart S.A.R.L.
1 rue de l'Est
75020 Paris
T : (1) 43 49 36 60
F: (1) 43 49 41 22
E: commercial@interart.fr

Ireland

Karim White
T 07740 768900
E: k.white@thameshudson.co.uk

Italy, Spain and Portugal

Natasha Ffrench
Export Sales Department
Thames & Hudson Ltd
E: n.ffrench@thameshudson.co.uk

Scandinavia, Baltic States, Russia and the CIS

Per Burell
T: + 46 (0) 70 725 1203
E: p.burell@thameshudson.co.uk

Africa

Africa (excluding South)
Ian Bartley
Export Sales Department
Thames & Hudson Ltd
E i.bartley@thameshudson.co.uk

South Africa, Swaziland, Lesotho,
Namibia, Botswana and Zimbabwe
Peter Hyde Associates
5 & 7 Speke Street
(Corner Nelson Street)
Observatory 7925
Cape Town
T +27 21 447 5300
F +27 21 447 1430
E noelene@peterhyde.co.za

Middle East incl. Egypt and Eastern Mediterranean

Stephen Embrey
T +44 7952 919866
E s.embrey@thameshudson.co.uk

Iran

Book City Co.(P.J.S)
P.O. Box 158757341
743 Shariati St.
Tehran 16396
T +98 21 88459950
F +98 21 88459949
E Semiramis@bookcity.co.ir

Lebanon

Levant Distributors
PO Box 11-1181
Sin-El-Fil, Al Qalaa Area
Sector No. 5
Building 31, 53rd Street
Beirut
T +961 1 488 035
F +961 1 510 659
E info@levantgroup.co

China (PRC), Hong Kong and Macau

Thames & Hudson China Ltd
Units B&D 17/F
Gee Chang Hong Centre
65 Wong Chuk Hang Road
Aberdeen
Hong Kong
T: +852 2 553 9289
F: +852 2 554 2912
E: aps_thc@asiapubs.com.hk

For China enquiries:
Marc Zhang,Beijing
E: aps_china@asiapubs.com.hk

Jiajin Chen, Shanghai
E: aps_sh.asiapubs.com.hk

Taiwan

Ms Helen Lee, Taipei
E: Helen_lee@asiapubs.com.hk

Korea

Zita Chan
E: zita_chan@asiapubs.com.hk

Japan

Scipio Stringer
Export Sales Department
Thames & Hudson Ltd
E: s.stringer@thameshudson.co.uk

Malaysia

APD Kuala Lumpur
No 22, 24 & 26 Jalan SS3/41
47300 Petaling Jaya
Selangor Darul Ehsan
T: (603) 7877 6063
F: (603) 7877 3414
E: liliankoe@apdkl.com

Singapore and South-East Asia

APD Singapore Pte Ltd
52 Genting Lane
#06-05, Ruby Land Complex
Singapore 349560
T: (65) 6749 3551
F: (65) 6749 3552
E: customersvc@apdsing.com

India, Nepal, Bangladesh and Bhutan

Kapil Kapoor
Roli Books
T +91 11 4068 2000
F + 91 11 2921 7185
E: kapilkapoor@rolibooks.com

Pakistan and Sri Lanka

Scipio Stringer
Thames & Hudson Ltd
E: s.stringer@thameshudson.co.uk

Australia, New Zealand, Papua New Guinea & the Pacific Islands

Thames & Hudson (Australia) Pty Ltd
11 Central Boulevard
Portside Business Park
Fisherman's Bend
Victoria 3207
T +61 3 9646 7788
F +61 3 9646 8790
E enquiries@thaust.com.au

For countries not mentioned above, please contact:

Ian Bartley, Head of Export Sales
Export Sales Department
Thames & Hudson Ltd
181A High Holborn
London WC1V 7QX
UK
T +44 207 845 5000
F +44 207 845 5055
E i.bartley@thameshudson.co.uk

Steidl Barcelona
Círculo Del Arte
Carrer de la Princesa, 52
08003 Barcelona
Spain
T +34 932688800
www.circulodelarte.com

Steidl Berlin
Bildband Berlin UG
Immanuelkirchstraße 33
10405 Berlin
Germany
T +49 30 4737 7014

Steidl Brussels
Librairie Saint-Hubert
2, Galerie du roi
1000 Brussels
Belgium
T +32 25112412

Steidl Göttingen
Buchhandlung Calvör
Jüdenstraße 23
37073 Göttingen
Germany
T +49 551 484800

Steidl East Hampton
Linde Gallery
25 A Newtown Lane
East Hampton, NY
11937 USA
T +1 6316045757

Steidl Hong Kong
Asia One
8 Fung Yip Street, Chai Wan
Hong Kong
China
T +852 2 8 892 320

Steidl Johannesburg
MAKER
Shop 2, Chester Court
142 Jan Smuts Ave
Parkwood
Johannesburg 2193
South Africa
T +27 11 447 6680

Steidl Lisbon
Rua do Norte, 14
1200-286 Lisboa
Portugal
T +35 1 936 250 198

Steidl London
Rough Trade East
Old Truman Brewery
91 Brick Lane
London E1 6QL
England
T +44 207 3927788

Steidl Los Angeles
Rosegallery
Bergamot Station Arts Center
Gallery G5
2525 Michigan Avenue
Santa Monica, CA 90404
USA
T +1 3102648440

Steidl Ljubljana
Galerija Fotografija
gallery and bookshop
Levstikov trg 7
Ljubljana/Slovenia
T/F +38 612511529
M +38 641664357
www.galerijafotografija.si

Steidl Madrid
La Fabrica
Verónica 13
28014 Madrid
Spain
T +34 912985537

Steidl Moscow
The Lumiere Brothers
Center of Photography
Red October, Bolotnaya emb., 3, b.1
119072 Moscow
Russia
T +7 4952289878
www.lumiere.ru

Steidl Moscow
Pobeda Gallery
4th Siromyatnicheskiy pereulok 1
Stroenie 6
Moscow 105120
Russia

Steidl New Delhi
Photoink
11 Aurangzeb Road
New Delhi 110011
India
T +91 11 23792097

Steidl Paris
Librairie 7L
7, rue de Lille
75007 Paris
France
T +33 1 42920358

Steidl Ravensburg
Buchhandlung Anna Rahm
Marktstraße 43
88212 Ravensburg
Germany
T +49 751 16737

Steidl Rome
s.t. foto libreria galleria
Via degli Ombrellari
25 00193 Roma
Italy
T +39 066 4760105

Steidl San Diego
Museum of Photographic Arts
Museum Store
1649 El Prado
San Diego, CA 92101
USA
T +1 6192387559231

Steidl Tokyo
POST / limArt co., ltd
2-10-3-1F Ebisuminami
Shibuya-ku
150-0022 Tokyo
Japan
T +81 3 3713 8670
www.post-books.info

Steidl Valencia
SLEEPLATEPROJECTS
Plaza del Ayuntamiento 19-3C
46002 Valencia
Spain
www.sleeplateprojects.com

steidl.de
For detailed information on all our
books, artists and related events
please visit us at www.steidl.de

Photos from the book William Eggleston, Flowers (see pages 38-39)

The Paris Photo—Aperture Foundation
PhotoBook of the Year Award Prize

Dayanita Singh
Museum Bhavan

PhotoBook of the Year Award Shortlist

Mark Neville
Fancy Pictures

Lucie Photobook Award
Winner of the Traditional Prize

Mark Peterson
Political Theatre

Nominated for a Lucie Award in the category
"Book Publisher of the Year, Classic Support"

Peter Badge
Nobel Heroes

Art Director's Club Deutschland
ADC Wettbewerb 2017
Gold in the category Design > Book

Tomasz Gudzowaty
Closer

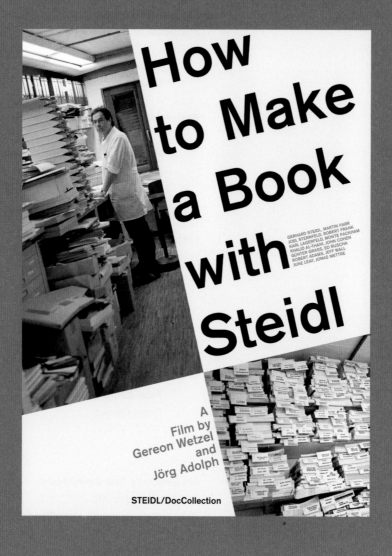

HOW TO MAKE A BOOK WITH STEIDL

Martin Parr describes his new book, Gerhard Steidl packs his suitcase, Ed Ruscha designs an ambitious artist's book, Günter Grass illustrates a new cover for *The Tin Drum,* Joel Sternfeld takes photos with his iPhone, Karl Lagerfeld walks the runway in Paris, Robert Adams rummages for vintage prints, Jeff Wall offers a tour of his new studio, John Cohen gives an impromptu concert, Robert Frank stumbles across a forgotten Polaroid...

For over a year, Gereon Wetzel and Jörg Adolph filmed on site at Düstere Strasse 4 in Göttingen, recording first-hand the organized chaos that is daily working life at Steidl Publishers. From book concept to design, from editorial and pre-press to printing, the film exposes the contemporary craft of bookmaking. Accompanying Gerhard Steidl on travels to artists' studios and galleries—from New York and Mabou, to Doha and Vancouver—Wetzel and Adolph also capture some of the unique characters and collaborations through which Steidl books come into being. *How to Make a Book with Steidl* is the 2010 winner of the Goldene Taube for Best German Documentary Film in Leipzig and the Goethe-Institut Documentary Film Prize.

DVD 90 mins PAL and NTSC
Languages: English with German subtitles
With a 48-page text book
in a clamshell box
5.5 × 7.5 in. / 14 × 19 cm

€ 15.00 / £ 12.00 / US$ 20.00
ISBN 978-3-86930-226-3

HOW TO MAKE A BOOK WITH CARLOS SAURA & STEIDL

This documentary film shows the story of creating Carlos Saura's *Vanished Spain*, a book of Saura's photos of Andalusia and central Spain in the late 1950s, and published by Steidl in 2016. As a young man the great Spanish film director Saura didn't quite know what he wanted to become: a motorcycle racer, flamenco dancer or a photographer. 60 years, more than 40 films and numerous awards later, film has proven Saura's focus yet his passion for photography runs like a thread throughout his career and life. Indeed his studio in Madrid today resembles a photographic museum, packed with curiosities, vintage Leicas and self-made cameras.

When publishers Hans Meinke and Gerhard Steidl set out to publish Saura's largely unknown photographic oeuvre, they did not anticipate discovering the compelling landscapes, villages, bullfights and people of another era that comprise Saura's personal portrait of 1950s Spain and transgress the propaganda imagery of the Franco regime. Neither did they expect the twists and turns of creating the book with Saura, an artist who resolutely calls himself a "photographic amateur." *How to Make a Book with Carlos Saura & Steidl* reveals how photos become a photobook, and leaves open the amusing question of who of Saura, Meinke and Steidl were ultimately the Father, Son and Holy Spirit in their two-year-long creative process.

Photography has been the archive of my memory. Carlos Saura

DVD 52 mins PAL and NTSC
Languages: English with German and Spanish subtitles
With a 48 page text book
in a clamshell box
5.5 × 7.5 in. / 14 × 19 cm

€ 15.00 / £ 12.00 / US$ 20.00
ISBN 978-3-95829-353-3

Steidl selecting the eight winners from 700 book submissions at the
Takeo Paper warehouse, Tokyo, September 2016. Photos by Yusuke Nakajima

In 2016, in collaboration with Yusuke Nakajima of Post bookshop in Tokyo and the Takeo paper mill, artists throughout Japan were invited to submit their book dummies for consideration for the Steidl Book Award Japan. Around 700 dummies were received, each of which Gerhard Steidl personally reviewed before choosing the eight winners.

The winners are:

Satoshi Hirano, *Reconstruction. Shibuya, 2014–2017*
ISBN 978-3-95829-408-0

Gentaro Ishizuka, *Gold Rush Alaska*
ISBN 978-3-95829-409-7

Toru Komatsu, *A Distant Shore*
ISBN 978-3-95829-410-3

Toshiaki Mori, *B, drawings of abstract forms*
ISBN 978-3-95829-411-0

Tomoyuki Sagami, *YKTO*
ISBN 978-3-95829-412-7

Tatsuo Suzuki, *Friction / Tokyo Streets*
ISBN 978-3-95829-413-4

Toshiya Watanabe, *Thereafter*
ISBN 978-3-95829-414-1

Takumi Hasegawa, *When Takumi Met the Legends of the World*
ISBN 978-3-95829-407-3

Born in 1983, Hirano Satoshi today lives
and works in Tokyo. His recent exhibitions
include the solo show "Reconstruction" at
the Nikon Salon in Tokyo and Osaka, and
the group show "45 Frames from PhotoVogue"
at the Leica Gallery in Milan. Satoshi's
work is held in collections including the
Kiyosato Museum of Photographic Arts in
Hokuto.

This book documents the large-scale redevelopment of the labyrinthine Shibuya train station in the heart of Tokyo's world-famous shopping district. Although many such ambitious construction projects are currently underway throughout Japan's ever-renewing capital in preparation for the Olympic Games in 2020, the work at Shibuya Station is in a particularly dense and active area—the world's busiest pedestrian crossing (where up to 2,500 people simultaneously traverse the street in five directions) is only a stroll away, while the station's nine train lines have remained operational throughout renovations. Mixing black-and-white and color images taken at various times of day and night, *Reconstruction* is both a collection of stilled moments from this bustling process of transformation and an unconventional portrait of Shibuya.

All great art is born of the metropolis. Ezra Pound

Satoshi Hirano
Reconstruction
Shibuya, 2014–2017

Book design by Satoshi Hirano and Gerhard Steidl
96 pages
15.7 x 11 in. / 40 x 28 cm
50 black-and-white and 44 color photographs
Flexible hardcover

€ 75.00 / £ 70.00 / US$ 85.00
ISBN 978-3-95829-408-0

Born in Tokyo in 1977, Gentaro Ishizuka
photographs with an 8 x 10 or other large-
format camera and has recently focused
on polar landscapes with motifs such as
glaciers, pipelines and traces of the gold
rush. Ishizuka received the Photographic
Society of Japan's Newcomer's Award in
2004, and a fellowship for overseas study
from the Japanese Agency for Cultural
Affairs in 2011. His book Pipeline
Iceland / Alaska (2013) was honored with
the Higashikawa New Photographer Award in
2014.

This book is Gentaro Ishizuka's documentation of the melancholy remnants of Alaska's gold rush of the late nineteenth century. The discovery of gold in the Alaskan wilderness attracted hoards of fossickers and industrialists, each hoping to strike it rich. Yet the subsequent reality was that the rush was unprofitable for most except the lucky (and ruthless) few; in time most diggers moved on to pursue new dreams and nature remained violated by their efforts. Ishizuka's photos of rusted shovels and machinery, dilapidated log huts dwarfed by the landscape, and eerie interiors and still lifes show the ghosts of human activity and how nature is slowly reclaiming her territory.

This body of work symbolizes how man's efforts to conquer nature only survive as an image of history in the best of Romantic traditions.
Frits Gierstberg, curator, Nederlands Fotomuseum

Gentaro Ishizuka
Gold Rush Alaska

Text by Ryuta Imafuku
Book design by Gentaro Ishizuka and Gerhard Steidl
120 pages
15.7 x 11 in. / 40 x 28 cm
60 color photographs
Clothbound hardcover

€ 85.00 / £ 75.00 / US$ 95.00
ISBN 978-3-95829-409-7

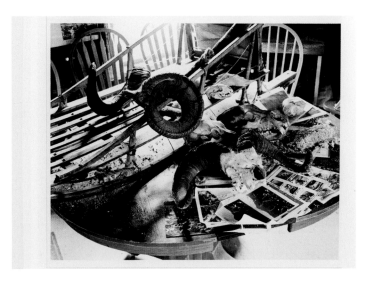

Born in Miyagi in 1969, Toru Komatsu
graduated from Tama Art University
in 1994. Since 1992 his video and
photographic work has focused on the
still-life genre. Today Komatsu lives
and works in Tokyo, where he is printing
director at Tokyo Lightroom and a member
of RED Photo Gallery, the site of his
most recent solo exhibition "A Distant
Shore" in 2016.

Since the Great East Japan earthquake of 2011, Toru Komatsu has
taken photos of trees in places that suffered damage from the
earthquake and subsequent tsunami. 50 of these images comprise *A
Distant Shore*, which documents the eerily beautiful aftermath of the
disaster.

On his travels throughout Japan Komatsu was particularly
fascinated by monumental rocky crags that seem like islands floating
on the land. Mostly scattered with pine trees, the crags are land-
locked but were once surrounded by the sea. Typically cordoned off
by ceremonial ropes, they are today treated as holy areas embedded
with the memory of their past—in Komatsu's words, "I imagine that an
island floating on the land still hasn't forgotten the ocean that once
surrounded it, even if the sea is now many miles away." Circular cut-
outs placed before each square photo allow the images in the book to
be experienced both as cropped circles and the full square layouts,
creating a sense of peering through a peephole or a telescope from
the wrong end, and transforming the photos into a setting for a
dramatic play while commenting on the limits of our fields of vision.

*Both photography and cinematic films are originally derived from
a single, round eye. By returning photographs to the perspective of
a single circular lens, Komatsu's work gives us a perspective on the
history of photography.* Sakumi Hagiwara

Toru Komatsu
A Distant Shore

Text by Toru Komatsu
Book design by Toru Komatsu and Gerhard Steidl
112 pages
11.7 x 11.7 in. / 29.7 x 29.7 cm
50 black-and-white photographs
Flexible hardcover

€ 55.00 / £ 50.00 / US$ 60.00
ISBN 978-3-95829-410-3

Born in Tokyo, Toshiaki Mori studied
design at Kuwasawa Design School in Tokyo.
After working in the scenographic art
department of the Haiyuza Theater, Mori
worked as an illustrator before taking up
photography. His solo exhibitions include
"Smell on day no. 16" (2012) at the
Tohoku Institute of Technology Gallery
in Miyagi, and "2B, drawings of abstract
forms" (2016) at William Morris Gallery
in Tokyo. Mori is a member of Japan's
Society of Publishing Arts.

B, drawings of abstract forms consists of dynamic and perplexing collages in which photos are digitally spliced and reconfigured, then colored and overlaid with grids, shapes and text fragments. Mori's underlying photos mainly depict Japanese industrial scenes and cityscapes, interspersed with close-ups of everyday objects such as light bulbs and shoes, while the text fragments include writings on the Beat Generation. Mori's "drawings" furthermore evoke the paintings of leading Beat figure William S. Burroughs, while Mori himself refers to his book as "On the Road in a Hazy Mood", a prismatic visual homage to Jack Kerouac's most famous work.

Toshiaki Mori has no intention of revealing the contents of his multi-layered collages of time and space. Toshio Kuwabara, photographer

Toshiaki Mori
B, drawings of abstract forms

Book design by Toshiaki Mori and Gerhard Steidl
96 pages
8.3 x 11.7 in. / 21 x 29.7 cm
50 color photographs
Softcover with Japanese folds

€ 35.00 / £ 30.00 / US$ 40.00
ISBN 978-3-95829-411-0

B,drawings of abstract forms
Mori"B"Toshiaki

Tomoyuki Sagami was born in Nagoya in
1977 and studied at the Tokyo College
of Photography. He has exhibited his
work throughout Japan, including the
"YKTO" series at Gallery Yamaguchi in
Tokyo in 2009 and "Out of Photographs"
at the alternative art space mujikobo
in Yokohama, which he has also co-run.
Sagami lives and works in Yokohama.

YKTO contains over 1,800 photographs by Tomoyuki Sagami of
buildings and houses constructed in Japan soon after World War
II. Presenting images taken between 2006 and 2017 in Yokohama,
Kawasaki, Tokyo and other cities (hence the book's title), Sagami
creates an archive for future generations of idiosyncratic architectural
styles that are disappearing due to changing laws and lifestyles, and
the ever-growing Japanese metropolis.

Sagami adopted a systematic, impersonal method for his project:
while employed to post advertising flyers in various neighborhoods, he
photographed the particular area he found himself in, block by block,
without any prior knowledge of its geography. The resulting images of
homes, shops, streetscapes, gardens and alleys are eerily absent of
people and free from any personal emotion or inclination on Sagami's
part. *YKTO* is a timely topography of a rapidly vanishing form of urban
existence in Japan.

*Do the cityscapes which are destined to vanish and the traces of the
living people there belong to the present? Do they tell of the historical
past, or are they prophesying the future?* Masafumi Fukagawa, curator
and critic

Tomoyuki Sagami
YKTO

Text by Tomoyuki Sagami
Book design by Tomoyuki Sagami and Gerhard Steidl
128 pages
9.5 x 12 in. / 24 x 30.5 cm
1,820 color photographs
Flexible hardcover

€ 40.00 / £ 35.00 / US$ 45.00
ISBN 978-3-95829-412-7

Tatsuo Suzuki was born in Tokyo in 1965
where he today lives and works. He began
photographing the street in 2008, and his
exhibitions since include those at Photo
Shanghai in 2015 and "Punk in Translation"
at The Horse Hospital in London in 2016.
Also in 2016 Suzuki won first place for
Street Photography at the ND Awards,
and was a finalist in StreetFoto San
Francisco and the LensCulture Street
Photography Awards.

This book embodies Japanese street photography now. Composed of black-and-white photos taken throughout Tokyo's bustling wards, *Friction / Tokyo Streets* reveals unexpected meaning and beauty in the mundane, be it in an image of a girl navigating a zebra crossing, cropped legs standing on a subway platform, shifting reflections in a store window, or a pigeon caught mid-flight. Suzuki captures the spontaneous gestures, glimpses and abstractions that comprise the best street photography. Yet as the book's title reveals, it is the conflicting and contradictory energies of the street that lie at the core of his project: "Through my own eyes ... I would like to express the tension, the edged frustration, the taut atmosphere and the feelings that beat, inherent in the city."

No one moment is most important. Any moment can be something.
Garry Winogrand

Tatsuo Suzuki
Friction / Tokyo Streets

Book design by Tatsuo Suzuki and Gerhard Steidl
136 pages
11.7 x 8.3 in. / 29.7 x 21 cm
130 black-and-white photographs
Clothbound hardcover

€ 45.00 / £ 40.00 / US$ 50.00
ISBN 978-3-95829-413-4

Friction / Tokyo Street

Tatsuo Suzuki

Born in Fukushima in 1966, Toshiya
Watanabe studied graphic design at
Tama Art University before taking up
photography. His solo exhibitions include
"Through the Frozen Window" (2015) and
"18 months" (2013) at Poetic Scape in
Tokyo, and "3 months later" (2012) at
Fukushimarch Temporary Gallery in Tokyo.

This book presents a series of diptychs of Toshiya Watanabe's hometown of Namiemachi in Fukushima—the first photo showing the subject shortly after the 2011 Tohoku earthquake and tsunami, and the second photo of the same subject from the same viewpoint a few years later.

Namiemachi was declared off-limits following the nuclear meltdown in Fukushima, yet when Watanabe did gain permission to return he photographed around his family and friends' homes, his former school route and areas where he played as a child. In some of the resulting diptychs only a short space of time seems to have passed between photos, with little changed besides the weather. In others, entire life phases seem to have come and gone—in one pair, a 7-Eleven first stands proudly before becoming a boarded-up relic; in another, a collapsed building is replaced by a vacant lot covered with foliage. "At first," Watanabe remembers, "I felt like time had stopped. But gradually the town fell into ruin, as if going against the current of history."

Toshiya Watanabe's "Thereafter" project engages with a deeply personal and universally timely question of how to represent the impact of the 3.11 tragedy. Charlotte Cotton

Toshiya Watanabe
Thereafter

Text by Toshiya Watanabe
Book design by Toshiya Watanabe and Gerhard Steidl
96 pages
15.7 x 11 in. / 40 x 28 cm
37 color photographs
Clothbound hardcover

€ 75.00 / £ 70.00 / US$ 85.00
ISBN 978-3-95829-414-1

Anna Wintour and Takumi Hasegawa

Jeff Koons and Takumi Hasegawa

David Lynch and Takumi Hasegawa

Zaha Hadid and Takumi Hasegawa

Bernard Arnault and Takumi Hasegawa

Yayoi Kusama and Takumi Hasegawa

Raf Simons and Takumi Hasegawa

Born in 1985 in Fukaya, Takumi Hasegawa
has held exhibitions of his photography
throughout Asia. In 2016 Hasegawa founded
the Architecture Model Workshop in Tokyo
which combines an atelier, workshop and
gallery, for the handmade production,
restoration and display of architectural
models.

Selfies are today an inescapable part of our visual landscape and our self-expression, and the ultimate dream of many selfie-takers is to snap oneself with a celebrity. Takumi Hasegawa fulfills this dream in this book, which presents him posing with his personal legends of the international rich and famous. From the worlds of fashion (Anna Wintour, Grace Coddington, Riccardo Tisci) and architecture (Rem Koolhaas, Zaha Hadid, Frank Gehry), to the arts (Jeff Koons, Yayoi Kusama, Thom Yorke) and luxury moguls Bernard Arnault and Pierre Bergé, Hasegawa's subjects speak for themselves. Yet the resonance of his project is more complex: in *When Takumi Met the Legends of the World*, designed as an intimate scrapbook or album of memories, Hasegawa's joy in each shot is palpable, but so is a sense of the seductive, false promise of fame.

Celebrity is the chastisement of merit and the punishment of talent.
Emily Dickinson

Takumi Hasegawa
When Takumi Met the
Legends of the World

Text by Takumi Hasegawa
Book design by Takumi Hasegawa and Gerhard Steidl
56 pages
11.8 x 11.8 in. / 30 x 30 cm
35 color photographs
Flexible hardcover

€ 35.00 / £ 30.00 / US$ 40.00
ISBN 978-3-95829-407-3

The winners of the Steidl Book Award Japan with Gerhard Steidl, Tokyo University of the Arts, November 2016. Photo by Yusuke Nakajima

William Eggleston checking his new book Election Eve, Memphis, August 2017. Photo by Gerhard Steidl

Released

Paris
2009

Before Color
2010

Chromes
Three books in a slipcase
2011

Los Alamos Revisited
Three books in a slipcase
2012

At Zenith
2013

From Black and White to Color
Steidl/Foundation HCB, 2014

The Democratic Forest
Ten books in a slipcase, 2016

The Democratic Forest. Selected Works
Steidl/David Zwirner, 2016

Election Eve
2017

Forthcoming

Flowers
Spring 2018

Morals of Vision
Spring 2018

Polaroids
Fall 2018

The Outlands
Fall 2018

Faulkner's Mississippi
2019

Ancient and Modern
2019

Burger Chef
2020

Family Album
2020

Egypt
2021

Louisiana
2021

Stranded in Canton (Video)
2022

Born in Memphis in 1939, William
Eggleston is regarded as one of the
greatest photographers of his generation
and a major American artist who has
fundamentally changed how the urban
landscape is viewed. He obtained his first
camera in 1957 and was later profoundly
influenced by Henri Cartier-Bresson's The
Decisive Moment. Eggleston introduced
dye-transfer printing, a previously
commercial photographic process, into the
making of artists' prints. His exhibition
"Photographs by William Eggleston" at the
Museum of Modern Art in New York in 1976
was a milestone. He was also involved in
the development of video technology in
the seventies. Eggleston is represented
in museums worldwide, and in 2008 a
retrospective of his work was held at
the Whitney Museum of American Art in
New York and at Haus der Kunst in Munich
in 2009. Eggleston's books published by
Steidl include Chromes (2011), Los Alamos
Revisited (2012), The Democratic Forest
(2015) and Election Eve (2017).

Flowers is a facsimile of the third of William Eggleston's rare artist's books, which was first published in an edition of only fifteen by Caldecott Chubb in New York in 1978. The original *Flowers* was a linen-bound volume with red leather spine and corners recreating the look of a photo album, and housed in a slipcase. Within its pages were twelve original chromogenic coupler prints focused on the theme of flowers.

Flowers, along with trees and other foliage inevitably feature in many of Eggleston's photos as part of the Memphis streetscapes and interiors that are his favorite motifs. But in this book the flowers take center stage in all their mundane glory—be it a kitsch spray of gladioli and carnations in a cut-glass vase, a single rose before a box hedge, or a forlorn bunch on a white marble tomb inscribed with the word "Mama." Along with Eggleston's *Morals of Vision*, also released this season, *Flowers* is a further chapter in Steidl's publication of Eggleston's artist's books in new editions that honor the design and spirit of the originals, while exposing their contents to the wider public for the first time.

I am at war with the obvious. William Eggleston

William Eggleston
Flowers

Text by Caldecott Chubb
Book design by Duncan Whyte and Gerhard Steidl
32 pages
13 × 9.8 in. / 33 × 25 cm
12 color photographs
Four-color process
Clothbound hardcover

€ 50.00 / £ 45.00 / US$ 60.00
ISBN 978-3-95829-389-2

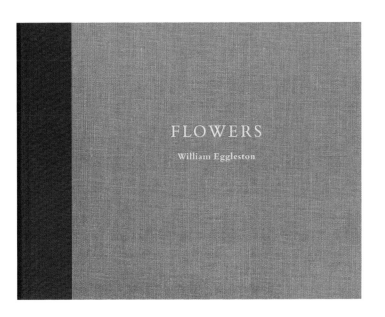

Born in Memphis in 1939, William
Eggleston is regarded as one of the
greatest photographers of his generation
and a major American artist who has
fundamentally changed how the urban
landscape is viewed. He obtained his first
camera in 1957 and was later profoundly
influenced by Henri Cartier-Bresson's The
Decisive Moment. Eggleston introduced
dye-transfer printing, a previously
commercial photographic process, into the
making of artists' prints. His exhibition
"Photographs by William Eggleston" at the
Museum of Modern Art in New York in 1976
was a milestone. He was also involved in
the development of video technology in
the seventies. Eggleston is represented
in museums worldwide, and in 2008 a
retrospective of his work was held at
the Whitney Museum of American Art in
New York and at Haus der Kunst in Munich
in 2009. Eggleston's books published by
Steidl include Chromes (2011), Los Alamos
Revisited (2012), The Democratic Forest
(2015) and Election Eve (2017).

When William Eggleston's second artist's book *Morals of Visions* was
first published in 1978 in a limited edition of fifteen, only a handful of
lucky people were able to obtain it; it has since become a collectible
rarity. That is now to change with this new Steidl edition, which
re-imagines *Morals of Visions* as a trade book for the general public.

The original *Morals of Vision* contains eight color coupler prints of
Eggleston's archetypal still lifes, landscapes and portraits which glorify
the banal and have since changed the history of color photography.
"There is no particular reason to search for meaning," Eggleston
has said of his work in general, a sentiment in contrast with the title
Morals of Vision which suggests that there are indeed principles of
a kind to be learnt from the images in this book. Yet the lessons in
photos including those of a broom leaning again a wall, green grain
silos in the fading light, and an off-center electric candle complete
with fake wax, remain Eggleston's own ironic secret.

*I don't have a burning desire to go out and document anything. It
just happens when it happens. It's not a conscious effort, nor is it a
struggle.* William Eggleston

William Eggleston
Morals of Vision

Text by Caldecott Chubb
Book design by Duncan Whyte and Gerhard Steidl
24 pages
13 × 9.8 in. / 33 × 25 cm
8 color photographs
Four-color process
Clothbound hardcover

€ 50.00 / £ 45.00 / US$ 60.00
ISBN 978-3-95829-390-8

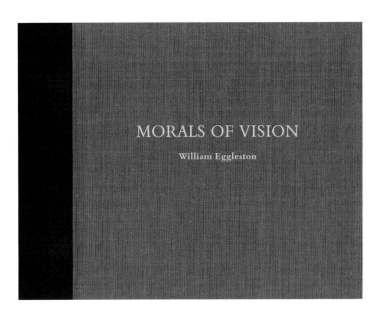

Frank checking the sequence of photos in preliminary dummy for the book
Was haben wir gesehen / What we have seen, Mabou, 2015. Photo by Gerhard Steidl

Tal Uf Tal Ab (2010)
You Would (2012)
Park/Sleep (2013)
Partida (2014)
Was haben wir gesehen / What have we seen (2016)
Leon of Juda (2017)

Known as his visual diaries, these six humble introspective volumes, published between 2010 and 2017, are the most important in Robert Frank's recent bookmaking practice.

The books imaginatively combine iconic photos from Frank's early career with the more private pictures he makes today. Black-and-white photos taken on 35mm film, including some from *The Americans*, mix with recent photos, often color Polaroids. Quiet still lifes, contemplative landscapes and urban scenes, self-portraits, and spontaneous endearing shots of friends, colleagues and the photographer's wife artist June Leaf show the life he lives today in their homes in Bleecker Street, New York, and Mabou, Nova Scotia.

With these images Frank creates seemingly casual layouts that recall the look and spirit of a private album or scrapbook, and comment on memory and the passage of time. Factual captions and short, sometimes cryptic texts are scattered throughout the books—Frank's thoughts, fragments of conversations, poems, notes.

When creating the first of the visual diaries *Tal Uf Tal Ab* in 2010, Robert Frank and Gerhard Steidl decided all in the series would be simple softcover volumes with an approachable size of 20.5 x 25 cm and a modest page-count. All books would be bound in a dark gray, leather-like cardboard, and housed in plain, inexpensive cardboard slipcases to create an archival feel.

Each volume was to have different colored endpapers, and Steidl suggested Fedrigoni Tintoretto Ceylon 140g, which was then available only in five colors. And so it was an easy decision for Frank: five books there would be—each a self-contained visual diary, but conceived together as chapters in a larger story.

Yet when Steidl visited Frank shortly before Christmas 2016, Frank revealed he had completed a sixth diary—proof that the photographer's passion for bookmaking remains an irrepressible element of his life. Steidl was delighted, and commissioned a further color from the Fedrigoni paper mill. Fedrigoni subsequently created black endpapers for *Leon of Juda* and guaranteed the production of further colors—thus ensuring the publication of future visual diaries.

Up seven steps to the door of Royal Hotel Sidney Nova Scotia.
Narrow reception desk big windows Moosehead above fire place.
Pay-Telephone in booth, dog on carpet sleeping.
Ring buzzer the owner Irene or Burt will come to
take your name give you key and Room 8.

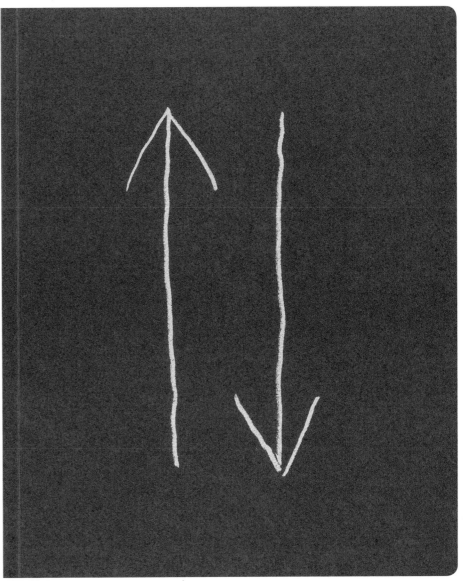

Book

Robert Frank
Tal Uf Tal Ab

Text by Robert Frank
Book design by Robert Frank, A-chan
and Gerhard Steidl
40 pages
Otabind softcover in a slipcase
8.1 × 9.8 in. / 20.5 × 25 cm
29 photographs / Tritone

€ 27.00 / £ 24.00 / US$ 30.00
ISBN 978-3-86930-101-3

Endpapers

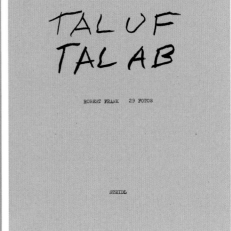

Slipcase

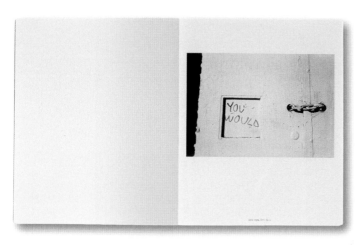

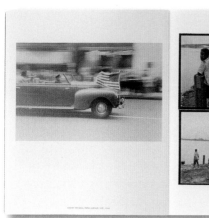

Book

Robert Frank
You Would

Text by Robert Frank
Book design by Robert Frank, A-chan
and Gerhard Steidl
48 pages
Otabind softcover in a slipcase
8.1 × 9.8 in. / 20.5 × 25 cm
41 photographs / Tritone and four-
color process

€ 27.00 / £ 24.00 / US$ 30.00
ISBN 978-3-86930-418-2

Endpapers

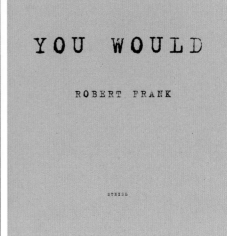

Slipcase

Hot soup
Not a travelogue
June! are you going to
tell the truth
Robert! almost_but first
I'm going to put
you in the cage
and I'll get out
of mine

Book

Robert Frank
Park/Sleep

Text by Robert Frank
Book design by Robert Frank, A-chan
and Gerhard Steidl
72 pages
Otabind softcover in a slipcase
8.1 × 9.8 in. / 20.5 × 25 cm
49 photographs / Tritone and four-
color process

€ 27.00 / £ 24.00 / US$ 30.00
ISBN 978-3-86930-585-1

Endpapers

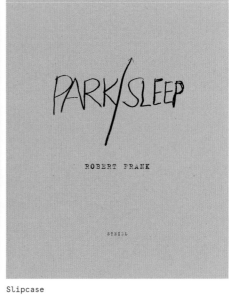

Slipcase

Book

Robert Frank
Partida

Book design by Robert Frank, A-chan
and Gerhard Steidl
56 pages
Otabind softcover in a slipcase
8.1 × 9.8 in. / 20.5 × 25 cm
32 photographs / Tritone and four-
color process

€ 27.00 / £ 24.00 / US$ 30.00
ISBN 978-3-86930-795-4

Endpapers

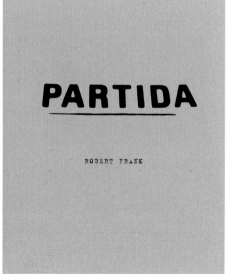

Slipcase

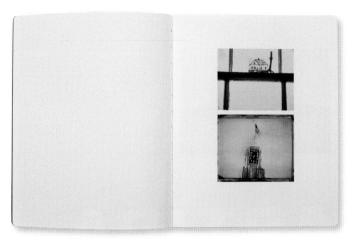

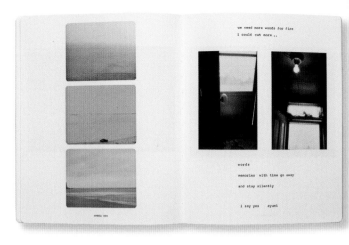

we need more woods for fire
i could cut more ..

words

memories with time go away
and stay silently

i say yes   ayumi

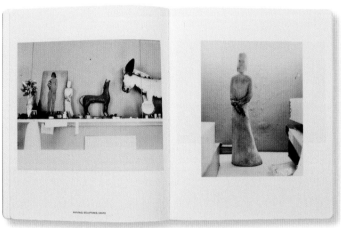

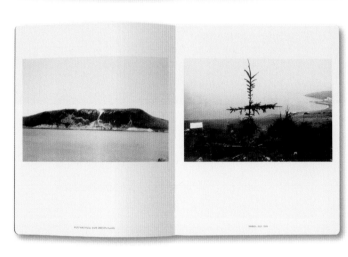

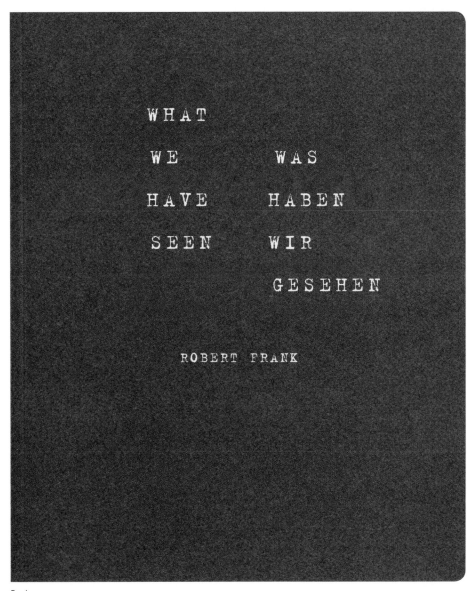

Book

Robert Frank
Was haben wir gesehen /
What we have seen

Book design by Robert Frank, A-chan,
and Gerhard Steidl
48 pages
Otabind softcover in a slipcase
8.1 × 9.8 in. / 20.5 × 25 cm
46 black-and-white and color
photographs
Tritone and four-color process

€ 27.00 / £ 24.00 / US$ 30.00
ISBN 978-3-95829-095-2

Endpapers

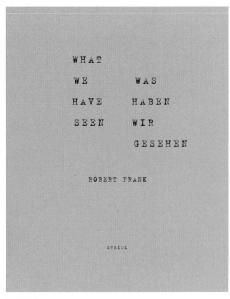

Slipcase

TINA HAQAR. PARIS, 1993

LEON OF JUDA

MARIA THEODORAKI

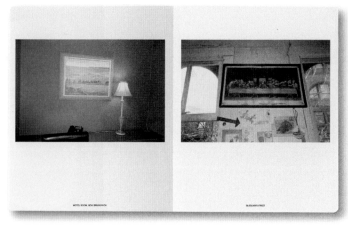

WAITING FOR TEDDY Oct 2006

MOTEL ROOM. NEW BRUNSWICK   BLEECKER STREET

DIXIE LEAF

WERNER ZYRD   SONNY BEATON

Book

Robert Frank
Leon of Juda

Book design by Robert Frank, A-chan
and Gerhard Steidl
52 pages
Otabind softcover in a slipcase
8.1 x 9.8 in. / 20.5 x 25 cm
33 black-and-white and 10 color
photographs
Tritone and four-color process

€ 27.00 / £ 24.00 / US$ 30.00
ISBN 978-3-95829-311-3

Endpapers

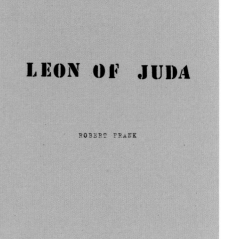

Slipcase

Vol. 1

Jak Tuggener

Die Insel der verlorenen Schiffe

1936

Vol. 2

Jak Tuggener

Polen-Wache

1942

Vol. 3

Jak Tuggener

Holzhäuser am Thunersee

linkes Ufer

1941

Vol. 4

Uri, Schwyz

1943

Vol. 5

Jakob Tuggener

uf em Land

1935-1945

eingeweiht 20 Juli 1953

Vol. 6

OHNE TITEL (Gallanz, Maag, Torres, Zährin u.a.)

Vol. 7

Jak Tuggener

Schwarzes Eisen

1935-1950

eingeweiht 1 November 1950

Vol. 8

JAK TUGGENER

DIE MASCHINENZEIT

1942-1951

Vol. 9

Jakob Tuggener

Ballnächte

1934-1950

(das Kolossennr) von Tuggener so benannt

eingeweiht am 2 April 1953

Vol. 10

Jakob Tuggener

Im Hafen von Antwerpen und Rotterdam

28 August- 8 Sept 1953

eingeweiht am 28 November 1953

Vol. 11

Jakob Tuggener

Eisenbahn   Schweiz
            Italien
            Jugoslawien
            Tunesien
            Frankreich
            Österreich
            Deutschland
            Holland
            England

II

eingeweiht 30 Juni 1967

Vol. 12

Jakob Tuggener Zürich

Grand Prix Bern für Automobile und Motorräder

Aufn: 1936-50

vollendet am 29 Juli 81

86 Bildseiten

Vol. 13

Vol. 14

Jakob Tuggener Books and Films

Limited edition of 1,000 boxed sets

Following an apprenticeship as a technical draughtsman, Jakob Tuggener (1904-88) studied typography, graphic design and film at the Reimann School in Berlin. Returning to Switzerland in 1931, he worked as a freelance photographer for industrial firms and illustrated magazines, allowing him to pursue his personal photography; in 1936 he also began making films. In the 1950s his work was introduced to an international audience thanks to Otto Steiner and Edward Steichen. Tuggener's uncompromising subjective style, influenced by 1920s German Expressionist film, inspired many young Swiss photographers including Robert Frank and Hans Danuser. The first comprehensive retrospective of his work was held at Kunsthaus Zürich in 2000.

Jakob Tuggener
Books and Films

Edited by Martin Gasser
Textbook bilingual English/German
All other books without text
Book design by Jakob Tuggener
and Gerhard Steidl
9.4 × 11.8 in. / 24 × 30 cm
Photographs printed in tritone
13 hardcover books and a DVD-folder
housed in a wooden box

Vol. 1 Die Insel / Bretagne, 1936
72 pages

Vol. 2 Polen-Wache, 1942
76 pages

Vol. 3 Holzhäuser am Thunersee, 1941
40 pages

Vol. 4 Uri, Schwyz, ca. 1942/43
28 pages

Vol. 5 Uf em Land 1935-45, 1953
144 pages

Vol. 6 Sullana, 1943
56 pages

Vol. 7 Schwarzes Eisen, 1950
128 pages

Vol. 8 Die Maschinenzeit, 1952
152 pages

Vol. 9 Ballnächte, 1959
152 pages

Vol. 10 Im Hafen, 1953
136 pages

Vol. 11 Die Eisenbahn II, 1967
152 pages

Vol. 12 Grand Prix Bern, 1950
96 pages

Vol. 13 Martin Gasser, Jakob Tuggener
illustrated textbook, 2017
96 pages

Vol. 14 Fourteen short films by Jakob
Tuggener on two DVDs in a folder

Limited edition of 1,000 boxed sets

€ 700.00 / £ 650.00 / US$ 800.00
ISBN 978-3-95829-328-1

Jakob Tuggener's key photographic motifs were conditions in the factory, simple life in the countryside and the glamour of high society. At the same time Tuggener was fascinated by railroads, ports, ships, car races and airshows. Through photography he sought to capture all facets of modern life in a world between dark factories and glittering ballrooms. From the mid-1930s Tuggener made book maquettes of all these subjects, each crafted meticulously by hand and featuring up to 150 original photos. None of these was published in his lifetime except *Fabrik* in 1943, his seminal *Bildepos der Technik* which has formed the basis of his international reputation and was reprinted by Steidl in 2011. Many of Tuggener's subjects are also the focus of his short films, whose style oscillates between the documentary and fantasy.

Books and Films comprises facsimiles of twelve of Tuggener's original maquettes, dating from 1936 to 1982, as well as a selection of his 16mm films on DVD. Both these silent black-and-white films and his photobooks contain no text, just as he intended. This comprehensive publication is the first occasion for a large audience to grasp the immense scope of Tuggener's work.

Tuggener's photography reveals him to be not only a painter but a poet, and indeed a rare magician and a curious kind of alchemist, who, be in it modest doses, transforms lead into gold.
Max Eichenberger.

Co-published with Fotostiftung Schweiz, Winterthur, and the Jakob Tuggener Foundation, Uster

Exhibition: Fotostiftung Schweiz, Winterthur, 21 October 2017 to 28 January 2018

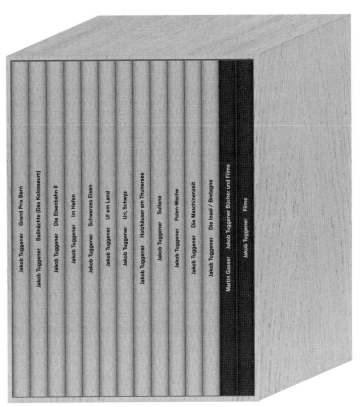

13 hardcover books and a DVD-folder of the short films, housed in a wooden box

42nd Street, 1979 contains Langdon Clay's 1979 photos of a quintessential strip of 42nd Street near New York's Times Square, showing its gritty neon charm before it became the more Disney/Las Vegas hub for theater concoctions that we know today.

Clay recalls the drab and dusty mood in New York City at the end of the 1970s: the once-exciting political sea change wrought by the Vietnam War and the Haight Ashbury drug experiment had given way to a sense of apathy, intensified by the aftermath of an oil crisis and the lingering Cold War. The particular stretch of 42nd Street between 7th and 8th Avenues had now shifted from the glorious home of gilded movie palaces of the 1940s to the shadowy site of porn theaters which many saw as the area's ruin. Yet here real-estate moguls saw potential to transform this heart of Manhattan into a mecca of tourism, framed by skyscrapers and shaped by commerce and fast pleasures. "It was with this coming change written on every wall that I sought to record for posterity that famous block between 7th and 8th Avenues," says Clay, "My only regret is that I didn't do the south side of the street."

Night became its own color. Langdon Clay

Born in New York City in 1949, Langdon Clay was raised in New Jersey and Vermont and attended school in New Hampshire and Boston. Clay moved to New York in 1971 and spent the next sixteen years photographing there, throughout the US and in Europe for various magazines and books. In 1987 he moved to Mississippi where he has since lived and worked with his wife photographer Maude Schuyler Clay and their three children. Clay's work is held in the Victoria and Albert Museum in London and the Bibliothèque nationale de France in Paris. Steidl published Clay's Cars. New York City, 1974-1976 in 2016.

Langdon Clay
42nd Street, 1979

Text by Langdon Clay
Book design by Steidl Design
128 pages and a gatefold
9.4 x 12.6 in. / 24 x 32 cm
100 color photographs
Four-color process
Clothbound hardcover

€ 75.00 / £ 70.00 / US$ 80.00
ISBN 978-3-95829-281-9

Born in Kentucky in 1950, Shelby Lee Adams attended the Cleveland Institute of Art where he was exposed to the photographs of the Farm Security Administration; these inspired him to take photos of the people of Appalachia, an ongoing project that has shaped his life's work. Adams' awards include a survey grant and fellowship from the National Endowment for the Arts (1978, 1992), grants from the Polaroid Corporation (1989-92), and the John Simon Guggenheim Photography Fellowship (2010). His work is held in collections including the Museum of Modern Art, New York, and Musée de l'Elysée, Lausanne, Switzerland. Adams exhibits and teaches internationally, and is curently developing his archive with the Center of Creative Photography in Tucson, Arizona.

The Book of Life presents Shelby Lee Adam's color photographs of four generations of the Appalachian people. Adams began photographing the inhabitations of the rural Appalachian mountain range in 1974, using black-and-white film and Polaroid materials. In time he also worked with color Kodachrome film, invariably returning to the Eastern Kentucky region where he was born. By 2010 Adams was photographing exclusively in digital color, and this book marks the first time he is sharing his color work.

Adams has consistently focused on the valleys and homes of Kentucky families, relatives and neighbors in a predominantly seven-county region. He has often revisited individuals and families many times over decades, distributing his photos and books while creating new pictures. This personal approach has led to the creation of genuine and deep relationships between photographer and subject, in which the subject is often involved in unusually creative ways, verbalizing the emotions they would like to express during the shoot, and where and how they would like to be depicted.

These portraits are, in a way, self-portraits that represent a long autobiographical exploration of creativity, imagination, vision, repulsion and salvation. My greatest fear as a photographer is to l ook into the eyes of my subject and not see my own reflection.
Shelby Lee Adams

Shelby Lee Adams
The Book of Life

Texts by Shelby Lee Adams and John Rohrbach
Book design by Shelby Lee Adams and Gerhard Steidl
184 pages
9.4 x 12.6 in. / 24 x 32 cm
85 color photographs
Four-color process
Clothbound hardcover

€ 50.00 / £ 45.00 / US$ 55.00
ISBN 978-3-95829-418-9

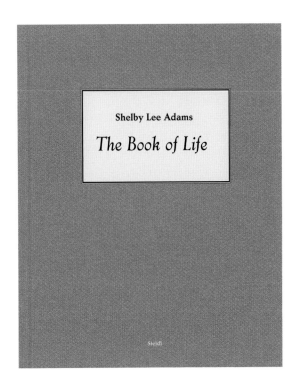

Ken Light is a social documentary
photographer with a particular focus
on America. His nine books include
To The Promised Land (1988), Texas
Death Row (1997) and Valley of Shadows
and Dreams (2012). Light has exhibited
internationally, including solo shows at
the International Center of Photography
in New York, the Oakland Museum of
California and the Visual Studies
Workshop in Rochester. Among his awards
are two National Endowment for the Arts
fellowships and the Dorothea Lange
Fellowship. Light is the Reva and David
Logan Professor of Photojournalism at the
University of California, Berkeley.

This book of Ken Light's earliest photos from 1969 to 1974 documents the social, cultural and political landscapes of America as they roiled with upheaval, and marks his transformation from a student activist to a concerned social documentary photographer. Light's frontline photos show people across race, class and political lines, and counteract the truncated memory of the sixties that has often been promoted by the media.

Light's journey through America begins with teenagers at the beach with their transistor radio. Here is the quiet before the storm: high-school students with their Eisenhower textbook, retirees playing cards and cafeteria workers quietly striking. And then, suddenly, the new, alternative worldview bursts forth: the Vietnam Moratorium, the Republican Convention, riots, POWs returning home, Nixon's resignation. *What's Going On?* reveals how politically divided the United States was as a progressive, more egalitarian world order was foisted upon it. It stirs long forgotten memories for those who were present, creates a cultural and historical legacy for the youth of today, and argues that much of our current turmoil is the result of cataclysmic changes of the sixties we have not yet absorbed.

Light shows us the collective movement forward, in love and in struggle, on both sides of the political divide, and exemplifies the power of photography to both reveal and form those movements.
Martha Rosler, *Aperture*

Ken Light
What's Going On? 1969–1974

Edited by Melanie Light
Text by Ken Light
Book design by Bonnie Briant Design
192 pages
11.7 × 13 in. / 29.7 × 33 cm
139 black-and-white photographs
Tritone
Clothbound hardcover

€ 68.00 / £ 64.00 / US$ 75.00
ISBN 978-3-95829-396-0

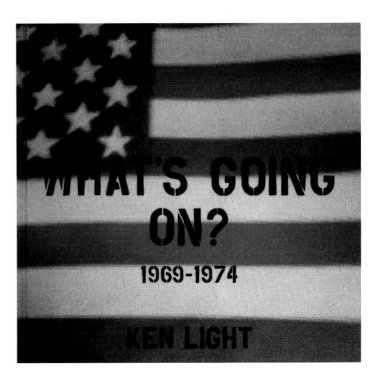

El Ejido, 2017, from Andreas Gursky

Regarded as one of the most important photographers of our time, Andreas Gursky (born in Leipzig in 1955) is known for his large-scale, often spectacular pictures that portray emblematic sites and scenes of the global economy and contemporary life. From the work of the late 1980s, produced after Gursky had graduated from Bernd Becher's class at the Kunstakademie Düsseldorf, through to his most recent photographs which continue to push the boundaries of the medium, Gursky's art has been driven by an interest in forms of collective existence. This includes depictions of massive man-made structures and huge gatherings of people in nightclubs, factories, arenas and vast landscapes, which together provide a sweeping visual record of our age. Steidl has published Gursky's Andreas Gursky (2015) and Bangkok (2012).

Andreas Gursky has been widely celebrated for his monumental, extraordinarily detailed pictures, often exploring contemporary global themes. This comprehensive book takes a fresh look at the artist's iconic images from the past four decades.

In a landmark conversation between two of the most significant figures in contemporary photography, Gursky talks to Jeff Wall about the sources for his photographic vision, while an essay by Hayward Gallery director Ralph Rugoff explores important but often neglected areas of the artist's work. Essays by art historian Gerald Schröder and writer-curator Brian Sholis provide new insight into key pictures, and artist Katharina Fritsch offers personal snapshots of her Düsseldorf colleague, creating a portrait of the artist in the round. Presenting the artist's most well known works – including *Paris, Montparnasse* (1993), *99 Cent* (2001) and *Chicago Board of Trade III* (2009) – as well as new, previously unpublished photographs, this is an indispensible survey of forty years of work from one of the world's most influential artists.

I only pursue one goal: the encyclopedia of life. Andreas Gursky

Co-published with Hayward Gallery Publishing

Exhibition: Hayward Gallery, London, 25 January to 22 April 2018

Andreas Gursky

Texts by Ralph Rugoff, Gerald Schröder and
Brian Sholis
Interview between Andreas Gursky and Jeff Wall
Book design by Graphic Thought Facility
168 pages
11.6 × 10.2 in. / 29.5 × 26 cm
100 color photographs
Four-color process
Hardcover in a slipcase

€ 50.00 / US$ 60.00
ISBN 978-3-95829-392-2

Distributed in the UK by
Cornerhouse Publications

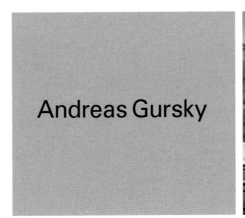

Slipcase

Book

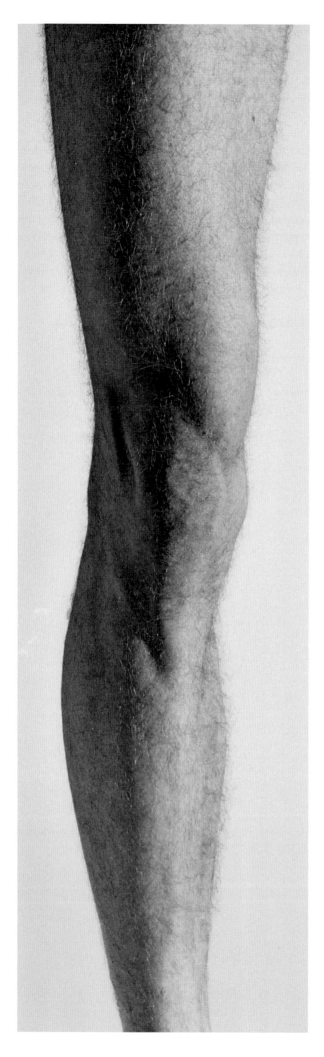
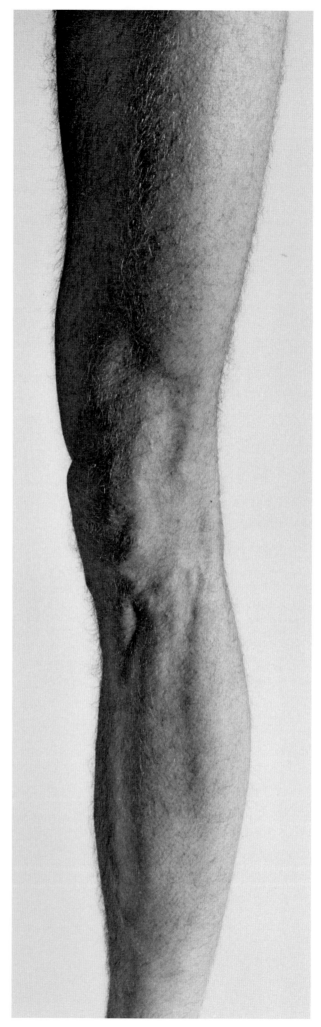

Born in Bern in 1944, Balthasar Burkhard worked in the early 1960s with Kurt Blum, then exhibition photographer at the Kunsthalle Bern. Burkhard succeeded Blum in this position and through the Kunsthalle's director Harald Szeeman came to photograph much contemporary art of the time, including the Venice Biennale and the famed documenta 5 of 1972. In the late 1960s Burkhard developed with artist Markus Raetz a series of photos on canvas of interiors, and in 1976 he moved to the USA, lecturing at the University of Illinois where he also held his first solo exhibition. He returned to Switzerland in the early 1980s where further solo shows followed, most notably at the Kunsthalle Basel in 1983. Burkhard later collaborated with the architectural company Atelier 5, taught at the École des Beaux-Arts in Nîmes, and in 1998 released his film La Ciudad. Burkhard died in 2010.

Balthasar Burkhard

Texts by Balthasar Burkhard, Laurent Busine, Florian Ebner, Abigail Solomon-Godeau, Martin Gasser, Ralph Gentner, Jennifer Gough-Cooper, Tom Holert, Markus Jakob, Thomas Kovachevich, Adrian Scheidegger, Thomas Seelig, Hendel Teicher and Stefanie Unternährer
Book design by Helmut Völter
280 pages and four gatefolds
8.3 x 11.4 in. / 21 x 29 cm
293 black-and-white and 47 color photographs
Four-color process
Softcover

€ 40.00 / £ 38.00 / US$ 45.00
ISBN 978-3-95829-342-7

This book presents the many facets of photographer Balthasar Burkhard (1944–2010), showing his self-invention as an artist and tracing the trajectory of the medium of photography in the later half of the twentieth century. Burkhard's work combines a sensitive understanding of the body as sculpture and the photographic image as a canvas, making him one of the pioneers in translating photography as a monumental "tableau" into contemporary art.

This comprehensive book coalesces Burkhard's early role as a chronicler of the contemporary art of his time, especially as the main photographer for Swiss curator Harald Szeemann, his conceptual redefinition of photography together with other artists, and finally his emancipation as a photo artist. It accompanies a major retrospective organized by Museum Folkwang in Essen, Fotomuseum Winterthur and Fotostiftung Schweiz, the Museo d'arte della Svizzerra italiana in Lugano and the Balthasar Burkhard Estate in Bern.

Nude photos. I never succeeded with nude photos. I have discarded the experiments. But the discarded photos are as important as the successful ones. I have discarded them because the absence of the other was not clear enough. Balthasar Burkhard

Co-published with Museum Folkwang, Essen, Fotomuseum Winterthur and Fotostiftung Schweiz, Winterthur, and Museo d'arte della Svizzera italiana, Lugano

Exhibitions:
Museum Folkwang, Essen, 20 October 2017 to 14 January 2018
Fotomuseum Winterthur and Fotostiftung Schweiz, Winterthur, 11 February to 21 April 2018
Museo d'arte della Svizzera italiana, Lugano, 9 June to 2 September 2018

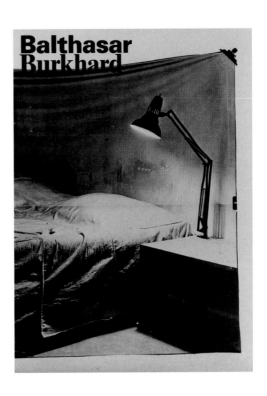

This book is a selective retrospective of David Goldblatt, a key figure in twentieth-century and contemporary photography. Starting from his earliest photographic searchings, it shows the foundations of Goldblatt's critical passion for photography, his social sensitivity and political consciousness. Also to see are his most recent photographs, always in tight relation to the changing situation in South Africa, his native country. *Structures of Dominion and Democracy* assembles many of Goldblatt's influential series including "On the Mines," "Some Afrikaners" and "Structures" with some less well-known including "Kas Maine," and reconstructs the history of their first publication in the international press. Reproducing original handmade dummies and working plates, the process of bookmaking and other diverse applications of these often iconic images are laid bare. In addition to texts by the photographer, essays by Ivor Powell and Karolina Ziebinska-Lewandowska explore Goldblatt's work in the context of South African political and cultural history, as well as his contribution to the wider history of photography.

David Goldblatt does not snatch on the world with a camera. He seeks to strip away preconceptions of what he is seeing before he goes into it still further with his chosen instrument – the photographic image. The "essential thing" in Goldblatt's photographs is never a piece of visual shorthand for a life; it is informed by this desire for a knowledge and understanding for the entire context of that life to be conveyed, in which that detail above all others has meaning.
Nadine Gordimer

Co-published with Editions du Centre Pompidou

Exhibition: Centre Pompidou, Paris, 21 February to 11 May 2018

Born in Randfontein in 1930, David Goldblatt is a definitive photographer of his generation, esteemed for his engaged depiction of life in South Africa over more than 50 years. His work concerns above all human values and is a unique document of society during and after apartheid. Goldblatt's photos are held in major international collections, and his solo exhibitions include those at the Museum of Modern Art in New York in 1998 and the Fondation Henri Cartier-Bresson in Paris in 2011. In 1989 Goldblatt founded the Market Photo Workshop in Johannesburg to teach visual literacy and photography, especially to those disadvantaged by apartheid. In 2006 he received the Hasselblad Award and in 2016 was made Commandeur des Arts et des Lettres by the French Ministry of Culture. Goldblatt's books with Steidl include On the Mines (2012), Particulars (2014) and Ex-Offenders at the Scene of Crime or Arrest (2017).

David Goldblatt
Structures of Dominion
and Democracy

Edited by Karolina Ziebinska-Lewandowska
Texts by David Goldblatt, Ivor Powell and Karolina Ziebinska-Lewandowska
Book design by Holger Feroudj
336 pages
9.4 × 12.6 in. / 24 × 32 cm
210 black-and-white and 173 color photographs
Four-color process
Hardcover

€ 48.00 / £ 45.00 / US$ 65.00
ISBN 978-3-95829-391-5

Ernst Haas was born in Vienna in 1921 and took up photography after World War II. His early work on returning Austrian prisoners of war brought him to the attention of Life, from which he resolutely declined a job as staff photographer in order to maintain his independence. At the invitation of Robert Capa, Haas joined Magnum in 1949, developing close associations with Capa, Werner Bischof and Henri Cartier-Bresson. He began experimenting with color, and in time became the premier color photographer of the 1950s. In 1962 New York's Museum of Modern Art mounted its first solo exhibition of his color work. Haas's books were legion, with The Creation (1971) selling 350,000 copies. Haas received the Hasselblad Award in 1986, the year of his death. His books to date with Steidl are Color Correction (2011) and On Set (2015).

Abstrakt is a collection of photographs selected by Ernst Haas for a two-projector 25-minute film he worked on until his death in 1986. The photographs span his entire career in color from 1952 to 1984. Many of the photographs were shown in *Life* magazine's fist color issue devoted to Haas' 1953 story on New York "Images of a Magic City," and in his 1962 solo exhibition "Ernst Haas: Color Photography" at the Museum of Modern Art, the first color retrospective at that institution. The photographs in this book show various abstractions—from street detritus, to torn posters and other found objects. Haas considered this project to be the culmination of his work in photography.

Ernst Haas was unquestionably one of the best known, most prolific, and most widely published photographers of the twentieth century.
William A. Ewing

Ernst Haas
Abstrakt

Text by David Campany
Book design by Thomas Lenthal
240 pages
11.8 × 11.8 in. / 29.7 × 29.7 cm
118 color photographs
Four-color process
Clothbound hardcover

€ 50.00 / £ 45.00 / US$ 55.00
ISBN 978-3-95829-393-9

David McMillan is a Scottish-born Canadian
photographer who began his career as a
painter, receiving an M.F.A. in painting
from the University of Wisconsin in 1973.
An interest in the tension between the
natural and the built environment led him
to the Chernobyl Exclusion Zone, where he
has photographed regularly since 1994.
McMillan has exhibited internationally,
and his grant and awards include multiple
Manitoba Arts Council Visual Arts "A"
Grants, two Established Artist Grants
from the Canada Council for the Arts, and
the Banff Centre's Barbara Spohr Award.

Since 1994 David McMillan has journeyed 21 times to the Chernobyl Exclusion Zone. Inspired by his teenage memories of Nevil Shute's *On the Beach* (1957), a disturbing vision of the world following nuclear war, McMillan found in Pripyat the embodiment of an irradiated city still standing but void of human life.

As one of the first artists to gain access to "The Zone," McMillan initially explored the evacuated areas with few constraints and in solitude, save for an occasional scientist monitoring the effects of radioactivity. Returning year after year enabled him to revisit the sites of earlier photographs—sometimes fortuitously, sometimes by design—thereby bearing witness to the inexorable forces of nature as they reclaimed the abandoned communities. At times his unhurried approach to picture making led McMillan to look at unassuming subjects, which gave rise to engrossing compositions. Above all, his commitment has been to probe the relentless dichotomy between growth and decay in The Zone.

When I first ventured to Chernobyl in 1994, the experience was thrilling and totally absorbing. I felt I had found a subject both inexhaustible and consequential. I wanted to make photographs describing something I hadn't seen before, which had the potential to be simultaneously beautiful and unsettling. David McMillan

Exhibition: Oakland University, Rochester, Michigan, 11 January to 31 March 2019

David McMillan
Growth and Decay
Pripyat and the Chernobyl
Exclusion Zone

Text by Claude Baillargeon
Book design by David McMillan and Gerhard Steidl
256 pages
12.6 × 11 in. / 32 × 28 cm
200 color photographs
Four-color process
Clothbound hardcover

€ 85.00 / £ 78.00 / US$ 95.00
ISBN 978-3-95829-397-7

DAVID McMILLAN

GROWTH AND DECAY
Pripyat and the Chernobyl Exclusion Zone

This book presents 35 photos of the Getty Center taken shortly before the 1997 opening of its new multipurpose complex designed by Richard Maier. Published to coincide with the twentieth anniversary of the center, the book reveals behind-the-scenes views of the building as objects from J. Paul Getty's painting, sculpture and decorative arts collections were being installed inside it.

In September 1997 The New Yorker commissioned Robert Polidori to photograph Maier's building. Within 48 hours he had made images of its exterior but remembers being unsatisfied: "The building looks great, but it could house anything really—a hospital, a university, or even some corporate headquarters." Polidori wanted to document the museum's interior, to capture what he calls "some sort of museological typology," and proceeded to photograph the rooms in which artworks were either freshly installed or still being so—sculptures under plastic sheets, golden candelabras resting on foam cushions, cardboard boxes containing unseen treasures. The resulting photos show the museum in the process of taking shape, expose the mechanics of curatorship, and reveal, in Polidori's words, a paradox: "The more a room may be filled with the helter-skelter of objects to be arranged, the more naked and raw the possibilities and intent of their placement become apparent."

Polidori is a master architect of the image of the interior. His photographs capture the intimacy of both the image and its object. They are a remarkable progression of visual phenomena. David Dorenbaum

Exhibition: The Getty Center, Los Angeles, 12 December 2017 to 6 May 2018

Robert Polidori
Synchrony and Diachrony
Photographs of the J. P. Getty
Museum 1997

Texts by David Dorenbaum, Amanda Maddox and Robert Polidori
Book design by Robert Polidori, Mai-Loan Gaudez and Gerhard Steidl
60 pages
11.7 × 10.5 in. / 29.7 × 26.7 cm
35 color photographs
Four-color process
Clothbound hardcover with a tipped-in photograph

€ 38.00 / £ 35.00 / US$ 45.00
ISBN 978-3-95829-383-0

Orhan Pamuk is a writer-artist who won
the Nobel Prize for Literature in 2006.
Born in Istanbul in 1952, Pamuk intended
until the age of 22 to be a painter and
was thus encouraged by his family. In the
1960s and '70s, as he describes in his
book of autobiographical essays Istanbul
(2003), he photographed the streets of
Istanbul to use in his paintings; his
early desire to take photos is explored
in the introduction to the illustrated
version of Istanbul (2017). The Museum
of Innocence is both a novel Pamuk
published in 2008 and a museum he opened
in Istanbul in 2012 that exhibits the
objects, pictures, papers and photographs
described in the story. The Museum of
Innocence received the European Museum
of the Year Award in 2014. Pamuk has now
been taking photos for over 50 years.

In the winter of 2011 Nobel-Prize-winning Turkish novelist Orhan
Pamuk took 8,500 color photographs from his balcony with its
panoramic view of Istanbul, the entrance of the Bosphorus, the old
town, the Asian and European sides of the city, the surrounding hills,
and the distant islands and mountains. Sometimes he would leave his
writing desk and follow the movements of the boats as they passed in
front of his apartment and sailed far away.

As Pamuk obsessively created these images he felt his desire to do
so was related to a strange particular mood he was experiencing. He
photographed further and began to think about what was happening
to himself: Why was he taking these photos? How are seeing and
photography related? What is the affinity between writing and seeing?
Why do we enjoy looking at landscapes and landscape photographs?
Balkon presents almost 500 of these photos selected by Pamuk, who
has also co-designed the book and written its introduction.

There is genius in Pamuk's madness. Umberto Eco

Orhan Pamuk
Balkon

Text by Orhan Pamuk
Book design by Orhan Pamuk, Holger Feroudj
and Gerhard Steidl
184 pages
6.9 × 9.8 in. / 17.6 × 25 cm
467 color photographs
Four-color process
Clothbound hardcover with a tipped-in photograph

€ 38.00 / £ 35.00 / US$ 45.00
ISBN 978-3-95829-399-1

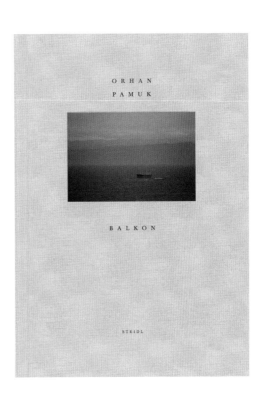

Orhan Pamuk, Balkon

Orhan Pamuk, Balkon

Christer Strömholm (1918-2002) was one
of the most influential Scandinavian
photographers and the recipient of the
1997 Hasselblad Award. Born in Stockholm,
in 1946 Strömholm moved to Paris where
he discovered photography. Between 1949
and '54 he joined the German group of
photographers Fotoforum, led by Otto
Steinert, and participated in their
exhibitions in Europe and America. Perhaps
Strömholm's most influential series
is "Les Amies de la Place Blanche,"
documenting the transsexuals of Paris'
Place Blanche in the late fifties and
early sixties. From 1962 to '74 he was
director of Fotoskolan in Stockholm where
he trained over 1,200 students, many of
whom would become leading photographers
including Anders Petersen, Dawid, Bille
August and Gunnar Smoliansky.

This book presents little-known photos by the legendary Christer
Strömholm selected by Gunnar Smoliansky. In the late eighties
gallerist Kim Klein proposed a small exhibition of Strömholm's pictures
at the Lido Gallery in Stockholm. Strömholm agreed and entrusted
Smoliansky with making a selection from his early 6 x 6 Rolleiflex
negatives. Smoliansky was delighted to do so—the planned ten to
twelve photos soon ballooned to 70—and he printed two sets, one
for Strömholm and one for himself. The photos date from the late
1940s and early '50s and show Strömholm's formative years in Paris,
the south of France, Morocco and other destinations. Most of these
pictures had never before been printed, let alone publicized, until
that exhibition of 1990.

*When I think about it, and when I look closely at my pictures, they
are all, in their own way, nothing but self-portraits—a part of my life.*
Christer Strömholm

Christer Strömholm
Lido

Edited by Gunnar Smoliansky and Greger Ulf Nilson
Text by Gunnar Smoliansky
Book design by Greger Ulf Nilson
96 pages
11.8 × 11.8 in. / 29.7 × 29.7 cm
42 black-and-white photographs
Tritone
Clothbound hardcover with a tipped-in photograph

€ 45.00 / £ 40.00 / US$ 50.00
ISBN 978-3-95829-335-9

CHRISTER STRÖMHOLM   LIDO

Guido Mocafico was born in Switzerland
in 1962, and today works in Switzerland
and Paris. A specialist in still lifes,
Mocafico's books with Steidl include
Venenum (2005), Medusa (2006), Serpens
(2007), Movement (2008), Stilleven (2013)
and Mocafico Numéro (2016).

It has long been Guido Mocafico's dream to photograph the master-piece glass models of marine invertebrates and plants that took Leopold (1822–95) and his son Rudolf (1857–1939) Blaschka a lifetime to create. This book fulfills that dream and showcases the Blaschkas' unparalleled dedication to their craft.

Originally from Bohemia but based in Dresden, the Blaschkas worked from the mid-1800s until the 1930s. From clear, colored and painted glass they handmade their intricate models of invertebrate animals (including jellyfish, sea anemones, starfish and sea cucumbers) as well as plants, only on commission and for purposes of study, mainly in Europe and North America. The objects were not sold to the general public and are today held in museum collections including those of Harvard University, the Corning Museum of Glass/Cornell University, and the Natural History Museums in London and Dublin.

It has been a difficult process for Mocafico to gain authorization to photograph the Blaschkas' creations, as most museums do not display these extremely fragile models. Yet Mocafico pursued the largest Blaschka collections throughout Europe and eventually gained access to photograph their hidden treasures in his trademark style. The result is similar to that of his "Nature Morte" series in that we constantly question what we see: a photograph, a painting, the object itself or a product of our imagination?

The Blaschkas spent between 30 and 50 years of each of their lifetimes, day and night, creating their glass models with unbelievable commitment. I was not scared to face the long-term job of photo-graphing their work, and it's since become both an homage and an obsession. Guido Mocafico

Guido Mocafico
Leopold & Rudolf Blaschka
The Marine Invertebrates

Edited by Patrick Remy
Texts by Alexandra Baudelot, Isabelle Pirotte
and Emmanuel G. Reynaud
Book design by Guido Mocafico
320 pages
10.8 × 14 in. / 27.5 × 35.5 cm
252 color photographs
Four-color process
Clothbound hardcover with a tipped-in photograph

€ 85.00 / £ 78.00 / US$ 95.00
ISBN 978-3-95829-398-4

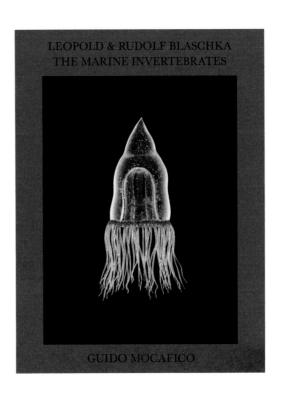

Timm Rautert was born in 1941 in Tuchola,
West Prussia, and today lives and works in
Berlin and Essen. Rautert studied under
Otto Steinert at the Folkwang School of
Design in Essen, and from 1993 to 2007
was a professor of photography at the
Academy of Visual Arts in Leipzig. His
books with Steidl include When We Don't
See You, You Don't See Us Either (2007),
No Photographing (2011), Josef Sudek,
Prague 1967 (2016) and Vintage (2017). In
2008 Rautert was the first photographer
to be awarded the Lovis Corinth Award.

Timm Rautert's 1974 series "Germans in Uniform", presenting a range of Germans in their professional attire in both a sociological and ironic manner, was first published in German by Steidl in 2006, and is now available in English in this expanded version.

For his project Rautert invited a range of public servants and officials to his Düsseldorf studio, where he photographed them in their work clothes—from a pastor, monk, Red Cross helper and hotel valet, to a more flamboyant drum major, forest warden and even a Santa Claus. Rautert depicts his subjects before the same neutral backdrop with similar framing and perspective, thus emphasizing how they reveal their characters beyond their uniforms. Below each photo are the subject's name, age and profession; at times personal quotes from conversations with Rautert during the shoot are also included. The result today is at once a complex portrait of post-war Germany, a nostalgic historical document, and an expression of the interplay between uniformity and personality that continues to shape society.

Rautert keeps reality in limbo. He creates a tension between staying in line and acting as an individual, between the uniform role and the person, between image and text. We leaf through the book, forwards and back, and remain puzzled by the real that comes with the roles.
Wolfgang Brückle

Timm Rautert
Germans in Uniform

Text by Wolfgang Brückle
Book design by Bernard Fischer
88 pages
8.7 × 11 in. / 22 × 28 cm
32 black-and-white and 32 color photographs
Tritone and four-color process
Clothbound hardcover with dust jacket

€ 45.00 / £ 40.00 / US$ 50.00
ISBN 978-3-95829-287-1

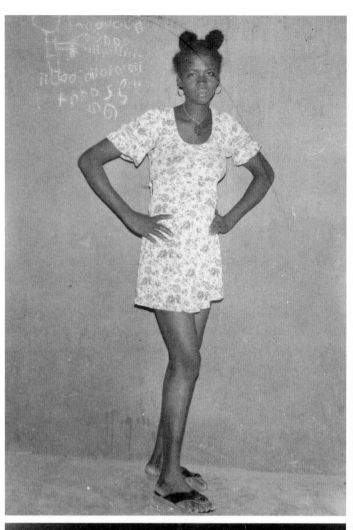

The studio photographs of Sory Sanlé and his participation in the
vibrant music scene in Bobo-Dioulasso give us a picture of a cos-
mopolitan city shaping its independent identity in the 1960s through
to the '80s, the heyday of West African independence movements.
Vintage photographs, seven-inch record sleeves and studio acces-
sories are all reproduced in the most extensive portrayal to date of
photography and music as key popular art forms with local, national
and international resonance. With the colorful full title of *Volta Photo:
Starring Sory Sanlé and the Good People of Bobo-Dioulasso in the
Small but Musically Mighty African Country of Burkina Faso*, this book
also includes essays on photography and sound in Africa as well as a
CD with hit songs by Volta Jazz, Echo del Africa Nacional and other
star bands.

*You need to make a memory, step by step, so that you can pass down
good memories to the young ones who'll come after you to those who
have yet to be born. You may no longer be here, but your images will
and they'll see them. [...] Photography is a witness to everything... For
me, without any photos, nothing actually happened.* Sory Sanlé

Co-published with the Art Institute of Chicago

Exhibitions:
The Art Institute of Chicago, 28 April to 19 August 2018
A4 Arts Foundation, Cape Town, fall 2018

Sory Sanlé
Volta Photo

Edited by Matthew S. Witkovsky
Texts by Antawan Byrd, Florent Mazzoleni
and Matthew S. Witkovsky
Book design by Steidl Design
120 pages and an audio CD
9.4 × 12.6 in / 24 × 32 cm
100 black-and-white photographs
Tritone
Clothbound hardcover with a tipped-in photo

€ 45.00 / £ 40.00 / US$ 48.00
ISBN 978-3-95829-400-4

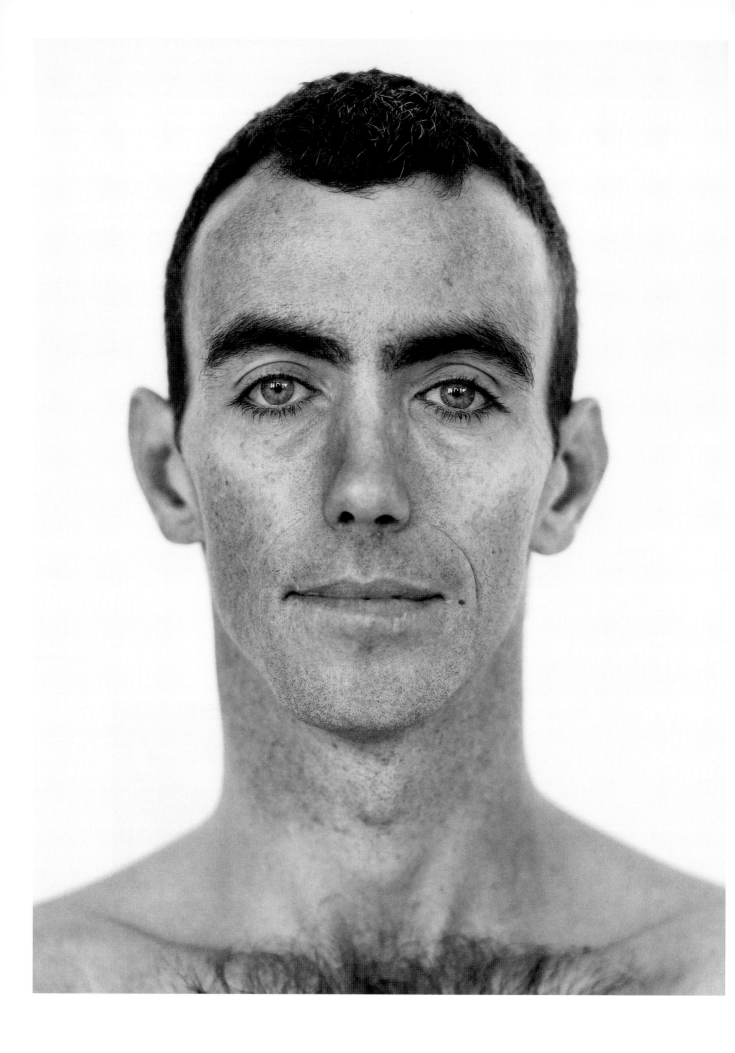

Six years ago Bryan Adams was approached by Trudie Styler to photograph a portrait story of homeless street vendors for *The Big Issue* magazine. That story inspired a more in-depth photographic look at these people who live on the streets of London and sell the magazine. *The Big Issue* is a weekly publication created by professional journalists and photographers, and sold on the streets to provide the homeless with legitimate income and facilitate their reintegration into mainstream society. Today *The Big Issue* is published in several international editions throughout Asia and Africa.

Adams' portraits are direct, compassionate and full of dignity. They depict character beyond social and economic circumstance, and can be seen as a continuation of Adams' 2013 *Wounded: The Legacy of War*, his portraits of young British soldiers who suffered life-changing injuries during combat in Iraq and Afghanistan.

To dismantle poverty by creating opportunity through self-help, social trading and business solutions. The Big Issue

Bryan Adams
Homeless

Book design by Bryan Adams,
Holger Feroudj, Gerhard Steidl
224 pages
9.4 × 12.6 in. / 24 × 32 cm
100 black-and-white photographs
Tritone
Clothbound hardcover with a tipped-in photograph

€ 58.00 / £ 50.00 / US$ 65.00
ISBN 978-3-95829-387-8

Sze Tsung Nicolás Leong is a British-
American artist, born in Mexico City in
1970. His work is an effort to picture and
understand the complexity of connections
and relationships in the larger world.
His series include "Horizons," "Cities,"
and "History Images" (published by Steidl
in 2005). He is a Guggenheim Fellow,
and his work is held in major museum
collections throughout the world.

On the night of 13 November 2015, Paris was convulsed by a series of coordinated attacks. Sze Tsung Nicolás Leong, not far from the strikes, did not consider taking photographs, weighed on not only by the difficulty of depicting a city already so exhaustively pictured, but more so by the impossibility of representing such tragedy. The next day Leong, wandering the city in the aftermath of the events, turned his camera downward to the ground, focusing on an aspect of the city we repeatedly look at yet largely do not notice. The resulting photos render a seemingly known city strange and unfamiliar. At first appearing to be abstractions or even aerials or views of the cosmos, they reveal specific details we would otherwise miss and which contain gravity in their apparent banality—from cigarettes left on the asphalt by mourners, to the footprints and broken glass of the night before, and the sawdust scattered on the sidewalks soaking up blood.

Paris, Novembre is a portrait of a city at a traumatic moment in its history and an exploration of how that history leaves its marks on the city's ground. Leong's series is a gesture of mourning and contemplation, seemingly of nothing and the reluctance to look, yet at the same time of looking closely and intently.

In the past, astrologers scrutinized the sky to understand the world. Leong scrutinizes the ground. Is he also looking to read some message in these images that he literally picks up from the earth? As if the ground were the key, the terminus on which all converges.
Thierry Grillet

Sze Tsung Nicolás Leong
Paris, Novembre

Bilingual edition
English and French
Texts by Thierry Grillet and Sze Tsung Nicolás
Leong
Book design by Sze Tsung Nicolás Leong
56 pages
11.6 × 8 in / 29.5 × 20.4 cm
20 black-and-white photographs
Tritone
Clothbound hardcover

€ 40.00 / £ 35.00 / US$ 45.00
ISBN 978-3-95829-395-3

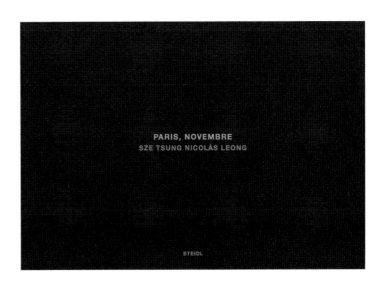

Born in Niagara Falls, New York, Shelley
Niro currently lives in Brantford,
Ontario and is a member of the Six
Nations Reserve, Bay of Quinte Mohawk,
Turtle Clan. Her multimedia practice,
which involves photography, painting,
beadwork and film, is directed toward
realistic and explorative portrayals of
indigenous people. Niro graduated from the
Ontario College of Art with honors and
received her M.F.A. from the University
of Western Ontario. In 2012 she was the
inaugural recipient of the Aboriginal
Arts Award presented through the Ontario
Arts Council. In 2017 Niro received the
Governor General's Award in Visual and
Media Arts, the Scotiabank Photography
Award, the Hnatyshyn Foundation's REVEAL
Indigenous Art Award, and the Visual Arts
Award from the Dreamcatcher Charitable
Foundation.

Shelley Niro is widely known for her ability to explode myths, transgress boundaries and embody the ethos of her matriarchal culture
in a wide variety of mediums including photography, installation, film
and painting. Niro creates photographic series that emphasize the
medium's inherent capacity for narrative and representation. She
pushes the limits of photography by incorporating Mohawk imagery,
re-appropriating traditional stories such as *Skywoman* and *The
Peacemaker*, and by focusing on contemporary subjects with wit,
irony and campy humor.

Niro marries portraiture, performance art and satire by having her
subjects and herself perform for the camera in ways that gently invite
audiences to rethink their beliefs and preconceptions about indigenous peoples and themselves. With compassion and deep insight, Niro
opens up the fault lines and desires of gender, sexuality and culture
to create images of freedom from the status quo in representation.
Photography was a medium that helped subjugate indigenous peoples,
but in Niro's revolutionary hands it empowers.

*The invention of narrative is surprising and can take you places you
might not otherwise go... I give thanks to my ancestors everyday. I
connect with them through my own imagination. The forward thinking
of invention and the inclusion of the universe makes being a part of
this world doable and positive. Everyone has their own story.*
Shelley Niro

Co-published with Scotiabank, Toronto

Shelley Niro

Texts by Ryan Rice and Wanda Nanibush
Book design by Barr Gilmore
228 pages with two gatefolds
12 × 9.8 in. / 24.8 cm × 30.5
70 black-and-white and 120 color photographs
Duotone and four-color process
Hardcover

€ 58.00 / £ 48.00 / US$ 65.00
ISBN 978-3-95829-401-1

Born in Berlin, Robert Lebeck (1929-2014)
studied ethnology before turning to
photography. For three decades he traveled
widely as a photojournalist for Stern,
interrupted only by a short interlude as
editor-in-chief for photography at GEO.
He received the Dr. Erich Salomon Award
from the German Photographic Society in
1991 and the first Henri Nannen Award
in 2007 for his life's work. Lebeck's
books with Steidl include Tokyo, Moscow,
Leopoldville (2007) and Face the Camera
(2016).

This book presents the diverse photo series Robert Lebeck made in 1968, which form an alternative view of the year when social conflict and personal rebellion against authoritarian traditions found their passionate and often violent expression. Upheaval, protest, perseverance and failure—themes that are not always explored in retrospective mythicizing views of 1968—are clearly expressed in Lebeck's photos, taken in locations from New York to Bogotá and Wolfsburg. Whether dealing with "Divorced Women," Rudi Dutschke in Prague, Robert Kennedy's funeral or Joseph Beuys at documenta, contemporary history encounters the integrity of photo reportage in Lebeck's work.

"The year of the student protests took place without me," Lebeck recalls of 1968 in his autobiography. "When the barricades were burning in Paris, I was working in Florida on a series about two murdered co-eds; when students began protesting in front of the Springer Building, I was photographing the christening of Hildegard Knef's baby; and when Russian troops marched into Prague, I was accompanying the pope's visit to Bogotá." A closer examination of Lebeck's contact sheets, prints and reportages made during this epoch-making year on behalf of Stern, then one of Germany's highest-circulation magazines, and presented in this book, reveal how Lebeck's photos, despite his own assessment, capture the social changes of the time.

[Robert Lebeck is] a photographer who really wanted to be an ethnologist, but swapped books and university for a camera and lucrative commissions for the world's best magazines.
Harald Willenbrock

Co-published with Kunstmuseum Wolfsburg

Exhibition: Kunstmuseum Wolfsburg, 4 March to 22 July 2018

Robert Lebeck
1968

Edited by Ralf Beil and Alexander Kraus
Texts by Ralf Beil, Fabian Köster, Alexander Kraus,
Aleksandar Nedelkovski, Stefanie Pilzweger-Steiner,
Annette Vowinckel and Ulf Erdmann Ziegler
Book design by Cordula Lebeck
320 pages
9.4 × 11.8 in. / 24 × 30 cm
150 black-and-white photographs
Tritone
Clothbound hardcover

€ 58.00 / £ 54.00 / US$ 65.00
ISBN 978-3-95829-419-6

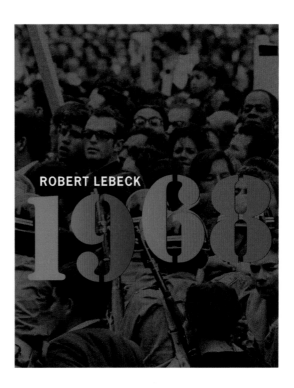

Born in Lancashire in 1942, Andy Summers
has enjoyed a prolific career since his
time as the guitarist with rock band
The Police in the 1980s. In the eye
of these experiences and influenced
by Robert Frank, Ralph Gibson and Lee
Freidlander, Summers became a dedicated
photographer. To date he has published
four photobooks including Throb (1983)
and I'll be Watching You: Inside The
Police 1980-83 (2007), and held more than
40 international exhibitions.

The Bones of Chuang Tzu is Andy Summer's interpretation of China. Influenced by many aspects of Asian culture since his teenage years and particularly the writings of fourth-century Chinese poet, philosopher and disciple of the wandering life Chuang Tzu, this book is a logical culmination of these interests. Rather than a collection of standard pictures of China, Summers uses the backdrop of the country to explore its symbolic and poetic tropes as he sees them, finding the unique lines, shapes and textures that repeat and represent that civilization in metaphoric terms—thus we find the lotus, the brushstroke, the dragon.

Summer focuses on aspects of China that are rapidly disappearing. But rather than romanticizing the past and seeing photography as an act of preservation, his pictures gesture towards the specific vitality of a culture. Take for example, Summer's photos of the Naxi orchestra in western China, through which he felt like he knew all these old musicians, but returning a year later he was dismayed to see many had passed on. "I found myself no longer shooting everything that confronted me," says Summers, "but rather slicing out pieces of my environment that would express something other: photographs as haiku. From Shanghai to Tibet, *The Bones of Chuang Tzu* reflects what happened."

With the same poetry and depth of his music, Andy's photographs from China show us his delicate visual regard. We hear what he is seeing. Ralph Gibson

Exhibitions:
Leica Gallery San Francisco, April 2018
Leica Gallery Salzburg, May 2018
Le Pavillion Montpellier, February 2019

Andy Summers
The Bones of Chuang Tzu

Text by Ralph Gibson
Book design by Andy Summers and Gerhard Steidl
120 pages
9 × 12 in. / 22.9 × 30.5 cm
80 black-and-white photographs
Tritone
Clothbound hardcover

€ 40.00 / £ 35.00 / US$ 50.00
ISBN 978-3-95829-403-5

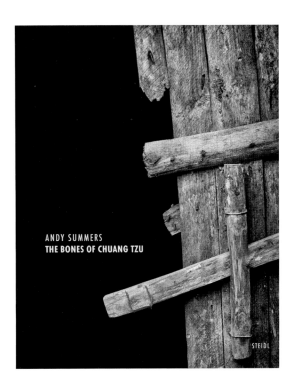

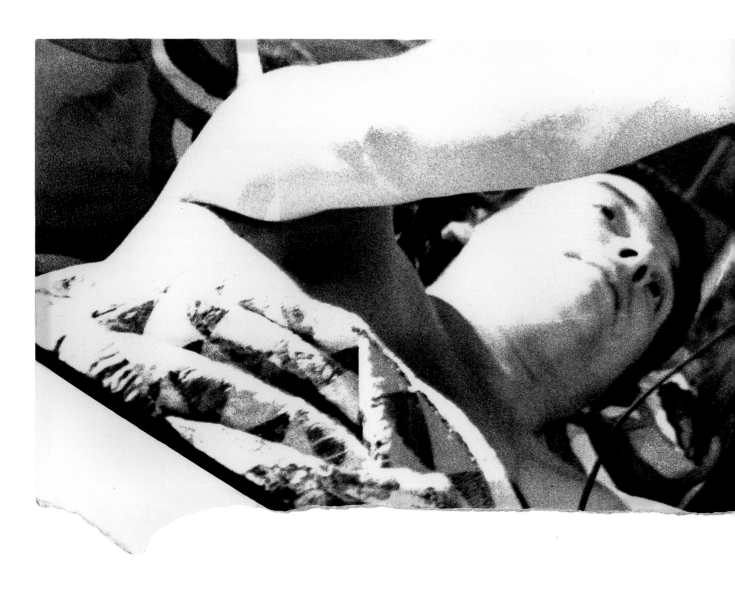

David Bailey on Gerhard Steidl

Monte Packham: When did you first meet Steidl?
David Bailey: I don't know. He's a myth isn't he?
MP: You think?
DB: Yeah. It's a preciseness. It's a very German thing, it's so precise, like Bach. They're so focused. He's probably one of the most focused men I've ever met. I don't know if it's good or bad—I mean I wouldn't want to live with him. But he understands photography.

Except from an interview in Monte Packham,
Concentric Circles (2010)

Bailey and Andy Warhol, 1972

David Bailey, born in London on 2 January 1938, is one of the most successful photographers of his generation. His career, in and beyond photography, spans 60 years. Bailey's books with Steidl include Bailey's Democracy (2005), Havana (2006), NY JS DB 62 (2007), Is That So Kid (2008), Eye (2009), Delhi Dilemma (2012), Bailey's East End (2014) and Bailey's Naga Hills (2017).

For almost 20 years now, Steidl has enjoyed an extraordinary book-making relationship with David Bailey. The first Bailey book printed and published by Steidl was *Birth of the Cool* in 2000, which is 26 cm wide by 33 cm high. Bailey was happy with the result and Gerhard Steidl asked him if he had an idea for another book. The answer was a resounding yes, and would result in 2002's *Chasing Rainbows*. When Steidl visited Bailey at his London studio and asked what size the new book should be, Bailey responded with his trademark no-fuss directness: "We've already made a book together, why changing now?" And so *Chasing Rainbows* is also 26 × 33 cm, as is every Bailey book made with Steidl since—and in the past decade alone we've published on average one new book each year. All these books form a Bailey Library, curated by the photographer himself. We can't wait to keep on expanding that library. Happy Birthday Bailey!

103

2005

When David Bailey asked his diverse subjects if they would agree to be photographed naked, none refused and none was rejected. The "democratic" results presented in this book form an all-inclusive, searingly honest portrait of mankind.

David Bailey
Bailey's Democracy
160 pages
10.2. x 13 in. / 26 x 33 cm
Clothbound hardcover with a tipped-in photograph

€ 45.00 / £ 40.00 / US$ 50.00
ISBN 978-3-86521-192-7

2006

My book Havana *is just a superficial look, not a soul-searching investigation, a quick impression of a place that is unique in its geographical position, being much closer to the United States of America than the space station. Both are places ordinary Americans cannot visit. To be one of the poorest nations on Earth, almost within spitting distance of the richest, makes the poverty of Cuba seem more extreme. Two countries with extreme ideologies; the small one proving that Communism does not work, the other proving that democratic paranoia does work if the power and the money are in place.*
David Bailey

David Bailey
Havana
176 pages
10.2. x 13 in. / 26 x 33 cm
Imitation leather hardcover with a tipped-in photograph

€ 45.00 / £ 40.00 / US$ 50.00
ISBN 978-3-86521-270-2

2007

In January 1962, still in his early twenties, David Bailey fulfilled a dream that dated back to his years in Singapore, when he served in the Royal Air Force. Heading to the US, home to the jazz music he so admired, Bailey made his first foreign trip for *Vogue*, accompanied by his model and girlfriend Jean Shrimpton. The impact of the couple's early collaborations set new standards that helped put Britain back on the world map of popular culture. The groundbreaking series that Bailey produced with his recently acquired 35mm camera was special. Newly freed from the confines of the studio, he shot rapidly on the streets and recorded the pioneer moment just before meeting Andy Warhol, and a year before his friends the Rolling Stones launched their own transatlantic invasion.

David Bailey
NY JS DB 62
72 pages
10.2. x 13 in. / 26 x 33 cm
Clothbound hardcover

€ 45.00 / £ 40.00 / US$ 50.00
ISBN 978-3-86521-414-0

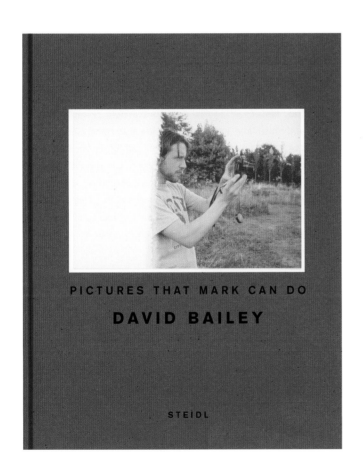

2007

"Mark is good natured. He finds the best in most things. To explain more would be too much. These are just pictures that Mark can do." David Bailey may be a master of the medium but he also readily accepts that photography is technologically driven. The snapshot is a part of our visual culture and many photographs have been taken millions of times, with just slight variations, such as the identity of the people in a family portrait. Bailey also takes such snaps, images imbued with a sense of ease and freedom yet which in his hands carry much greater weight and significance. He believes these photographs appear so easy that even Mark, his assistant, could have made them—and so this quip became the title of this book.

David Bailey
Pictures that Mark Can Do
176 pages
10.2. x 13 in. / 26 x 33 cm
Clothbound hardcover with a tipped-in photograph

€ 45.00 / £ 40.00 / US$ 50.00
ISBN 978-3-86521-367-9

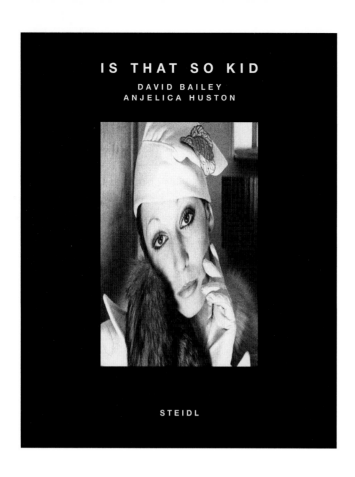

2008

"Is that so kid," was a typical reaction by the film director, John Huston, father of Anjelica. In 1973 Bailey conducted all his major fashion shoots for British *Vogue* with actress and then sometimes model, Anjelica Huston. The book is a record of their photographic collaboration.

David Bailey
Is That So Kid
72 pages
10.2. x 13 in. / 26 x 33 cm
Clothbound hardcover with a tipped-in photograph

€ 45.00 / £ 40.00 / US$ 50.00
ISBN 978-3-86521-632-8

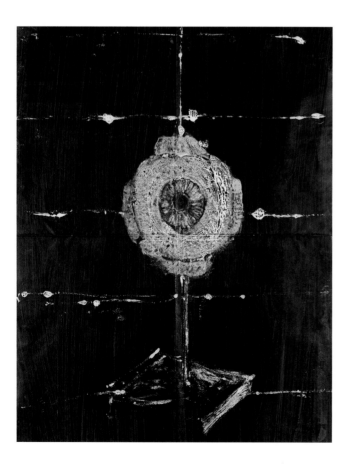

2009

Eye presents a selection of Baileys photographs spanning from 1962 to 2008. Mostly black-and-white, some in color, they feature influential directors, artists, fashion designers and musicians, including Andy Warhol, Henri Cartier-Bresson, Yves Saint Laurent, John Huston and Ellsworth Kelly. Despite the broad cross-section of subjects and the different creative spheres they inhabit, Bailey approaches them all with the same, egalitarian attitude. Crowned with cover art by Damien Hirst, Bailey's *Eye* reveals unexpected facets of the creative minds who have defined and in many cases continue to shape contemporary culture.

David Bailey
Eye
188 pages
10.2. x 13 in. / 26 x 33 cm
Clothbound hardcover

€ 45.00 / £ 40.00 / US$ 50.00
ISBN 978-3-86521-708-0

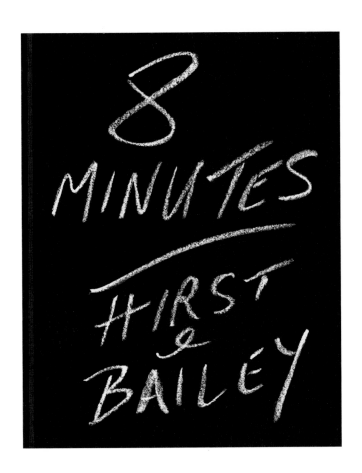

2009

The premise of this book couldn't be simpler: 130 photographs of Damien Hirst taken by David Bailey during a single shoot lasting eight minutes. Each pose is spontaneous and determined not by Bailey but by Hirst, who mocks the camera with his tongue poked out, mouth open wide and hands pulling at his cheeks. These photos are humble and unrehearsed, and so continue the sprit of *Bailey's Democracy* (2005) in which Bailey photographed a cross section of naked subjects, shunning issues of composition, lighting and digital manipulation. Renouncing text and even a title page, *8 Minutes* resists formulaic over-designed coffee-table publications. Bailey's roguish message: what you see is what you get.

```
David Bailey
8 Minutes
160 pages
10.2. x 13 in. / 26 x 33 cm
Clothbound hardcover

€ 45.00 / £ 40.00 / US$ 50.00
ISBN 978-3-86521-864-3
```

2010

This book combines Bailey's 2010 color photographs of still-life flowers and skulls, with black-and-white contacts of his iconic celebrity portraiture and fashion work from the 1960s. One might analyze these series in light of the vanitas tradition—indeed such a reading is tempting when comparing images of wilting roses with contacts of the young Brian Jones and John Lennon, who are unaware of the fates that will befall them. But perhaps this is all too much, and Bailey himself would probably say so. For him, the flowers, skulls and contacts are simply different projects that he was working on simultaneously and decided to combine because he likes the idea of "eclectic collections". Enough said.

```
David Bailey
Flowers, Skulls, Contacts
240 pages
10.2. x 13 in. / 26 x 33 cm
Imitation leather hardcover with a tipped-in photograph

€ 45.00 / £ 40.00 / US$ 50.00
ISBN 978-3-86930-128-0
```

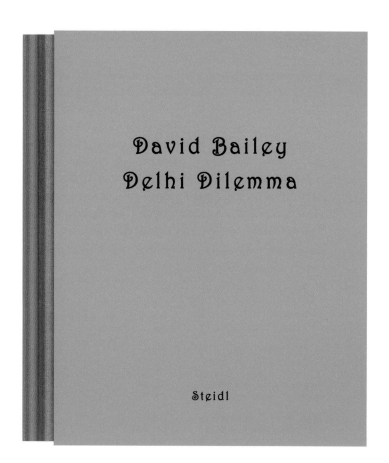

2012

How does one photograph Delhi without the results looking like clichéd, tourist-friendly images from the pages of *National Geographic*? How does a photographer of David Bailey's standing portray India without seeming condescending? Bailey has been to India 15 times, and in these photographs he avoids depicting the cultural and economic differences between East and West that can make photos of the country seem overly didactic. Instead, he depicts the colors, textures and people that characterize Delhi—a magenta sari, an infant walking down a rust-colored road, a bright blue plastic tarpaulin—and so creates a portrait of the city that is sensitive without being self-indulgent.

David Bailey
Delhi Dilemma
440 pages
10.2. x 13 in. / 26 x 33 cm
Two clothbound hardcovers in a sleeve

€ 95.00 / £ 85.00 / US$ 125.00
ISBN 978-3-86521-991-6

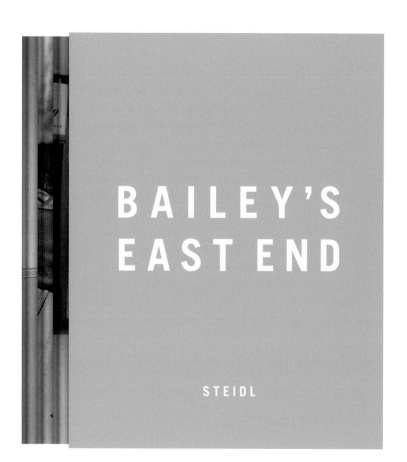

2014

The idea for a book on the East End formed sometime in the 1980s. The London Docks had already closed down or were starting to. I chose to shoot mainly in the districts of Silvertown and Canning Town. I have over the years spent many weekends shooting whatever took my fancy. The other two times I had bursts of photographic energy in the East End were in the 1960s and from about 2004 to 2010. These were my three key periods to draw pictures from, instead of just trolling through the last fifty years of archives. David Bailey

David Bailey
Bailey's East End
464 pages
10.2. x 13 in. / 26 x 33 cm
Three clothbound hardcovers in a slipcase

€ 98.00 / £ 85.00 / US$ 125.00
ISBN 978-3-86930-534-9

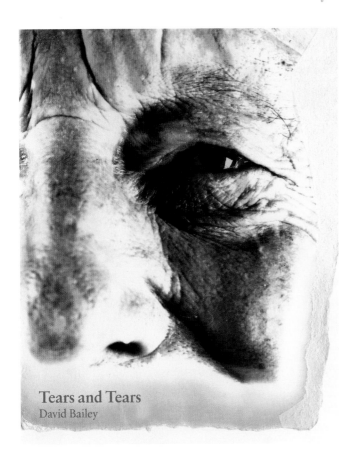

Tears and Tears
David Bailey

2015

Determining the perfect exposure time for a photographic print in a traditional darkroom can be time-consuming and tedious, and David Bailey has never had much patience for it. Normally a photographer makes a number of test strips, each showing different exposure times; but Bailey has always just intuitively torn off strips of the unexposed paper to find the desired result: "I would usually have it in the bag after three tears." Over the decades he has kept his "test tears," re-fixing and washing them to preserve the unpredictable and unique qualities of these "accidents." This book contains the best of Bailey's tears, which transform some of his most famous motifs into fascinating abstract pictures through their torn edges and myriad tones.

David Bailey
Tears and Tears
96 pages
10.2. x 13 in. / 26 x 33 cm
Clothbound hardcover

€ 45.00 / £ 40.00 / US$ 50.00
ISBN 978-3-86930-989-7

2017

This book is David Bailey's portrayal of the landscapes and personalities of the mystical and densely forested Naga Hills, part of the complex mountain barrier between India and Myanmar (Burma), and home to the Naga tribes, "those with pierced ears" in Burmese. Bailey's desire to visit the Naga Hills has been with him since youth, yet access had been continually restricted because of war and unrest—until 2012 when that wish finally became a reality. Bailey had initially wanted to photograph the story of the last headhunters in the region, but in typical Bailey style, he needed to improvise when things didn't quite go to plan: he recalls for example cutting though difficult terrain, becoming lost for hours, only to be discovered by armed men who directed him to a party at a guard post, where he proceeded to dance the night away with the soldiers... This is the newest book exploring Bailey's ongoing fascination with India, following *Delhi Dilemma* of 2012, and by no means the last—for in Bailey's words, "India seems endless."

David Bailey
Bailey's Naga Hills
176 pages
10.2. x 13 in. / 26 x 33 cm
Imitation leather hardcover with a tipped-in photograph

€ 45.00 / £ 40.00 / US$ 50.00
ISBN 978-3-95829-170-6

William Eggleston

Araki

Boris Mikhailov

Juergen Teller, born in Erlangen, Germany,
in 1964, studied at the Bayerische
Staatslehranstalt für Photographie in
Munich. His work has been published in
influential magazines such as Vogue,
System, i-D, POP and Arena Homme+, and
has been the subject of solo exhibitions
including those at the Institute of
Contemporary Arts in London, the Fondation
Cartier pour l'art contemporain in Paris,
and Martin-Gropius-Bau in Berlin. Teller
won the prestigious Citibank Photography
Prize in 2003, and has published numerous
monographs with Steidl including Louis
XV (2005), Marc Jacobs Advertising,
1998-2009 (2009) and Enjoy Your Life! Mit
dem Teller nach Bonn (2016).

This season sees the release of three new books in Juergen Teller's original and beloved "Masters" series. Teller made his first *Master* in 2005 as an homage to everything he believes is a master or masterful—be it a chef like Fergus Henderson, an artist like David Hamilton, his own grandmother, Kurt Cobain, or a landscape—as well as a tongue-in-cheek recognition of himself as a master of his own photographic identity. The concept was simple: to produce an ongoing series of humble booklets, each at the same small size, with no text and as little design as possible, and bound as stapled softcovers in different colored cardboards—an antithesis to the standard overblown coffee-table book.

Like past volumes in the series, *Masters IV, V*, and *VI* feature an unpredictable mix of Teller's eclectic photography: be it his unorthodox fashion work, still lifes and landscapes, celebrity and self-portraits, or images that slip between these genres. These books are dedicated to three of Teller's most important masters who have influenced both his work and outlook on life—Boris Mikhailov, Araki and William Eggleston—and feature new portraits of these photographers.

I don't like taking a sly picture on the side. I like the direct approach. I want to be as honest to myself and the subject as possible. And I'm depending on their humanness to come through. Juergen Teller

Juergen Teller
The Master IV: Boris Mikhailov
The Master V: Araki
The Master VI: William Eggleston

Book design by Juergen Teller
6.9 × 9.1 in. / 17.5 × 23 cm
Four-color process
Stapled softcovers

The Master IV: Boris Mikhailov
48 pages
28 color photographs

€ 18.00 / £ 15.00 / US$ 20.00
ISBN 978-3-86930-496-0

‖‖‖‖ ‖‖‖ ‖‖‖ ‖‖ ‖‖‖‖‖ ‖‖‖‖‖‖‖‖ ‖‖‖‖

The Master V: Araki
48 pages
28 color photographs

€ 18.00 / £ 15.00 / US$ 20.00
ISBN 978-3-95829-404-2

‖‖‖‖ ‖‖‖ ‖ ‖‖‖ ‖‖‖‖‖‖‖ ‖‖‖‖ ‖‖ ‖‖‖ ‖‖ ‖‖

The Master VI: William Eggleston
48 pages
28 color photographs

€ 18.00 / £ 15.00 / US$ 20.00
ISBN 978-3-95829-417-2

‖‖‖‖ ‖‖‖ ‖ ‖‖‖ ‖‖‖‖‖‖‖‖ ‖‖‖‖ ‖‖ ‖ ‖‖‖ ‖

The Master IV

The Master V   The Master VI

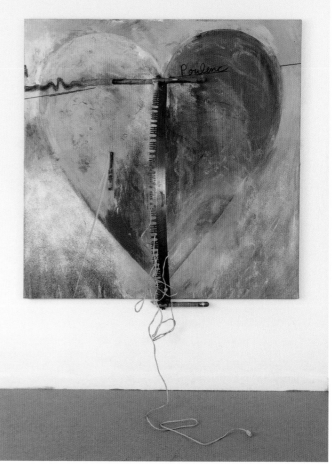

Born in 1935 in Cincinnati, Ohio, Jim
Dine completed a Bachelor of Fine Arts
at Ohio University in 1957 and has since
become one of the most profound and
prolific contemporary artists. Dine's
unparalleled career spans 60 years, and
his work is held in numerous private and
public collections. His books with Steidl
include Birds (2001), The Photographs, so
far (2003), Hot Dream (52 Books) (2008),
A Printmaker's Document (2013) and My
Letter to the Troops (2017).

This book is the catalogue to Jim Dine's upcoming comprehensive
exhibition at the Centre Pompidou in Paris, covering over five decades
of his varied and prodigious output. Over the past years Dine has
donated large personal selections of his art to museums across
Europe and the US, including the British Museum, the Albertina in
Vienna, the Museum of Fine Arts in Boston and the San Francisco
Museum of Modern Art. One such generous gift to the Centre
Pompidou, consisting of 28 paintings and sculptures from 1961 to
the present, is the subject of this book. Featuring double-page
reproductions of each work—covering Dine's major motifs including
his hearts, bathrobes, birds, self-portraits and tools—Also 9 poems
pertaining to Paris 1968–2018, supplemented with vintage photos, this
book is the most detailed survey to date of one of the most important
contemporary artists.

Anything can be anything. Jim Dine

Co-published with Editions du Centre Pompidou

Exhibition: Centre Pompidou, Paris, February to April 2018

Jim Dine
Paris
Reconnaissance

Bilingual edition (English / French)
Text and poems by Jim Dine
Book design by Jim Dine, Duncan Whyte,
Gerhard Steidl
176 pages
11.6 × 12.4 in. / 24 × 32 cm
20 black-and-white and 30 color images
Four-color process
Hardcover

€ 35.00 / £ 30.00 / US$ 45.00
ISBN 978-3-95829-388-5

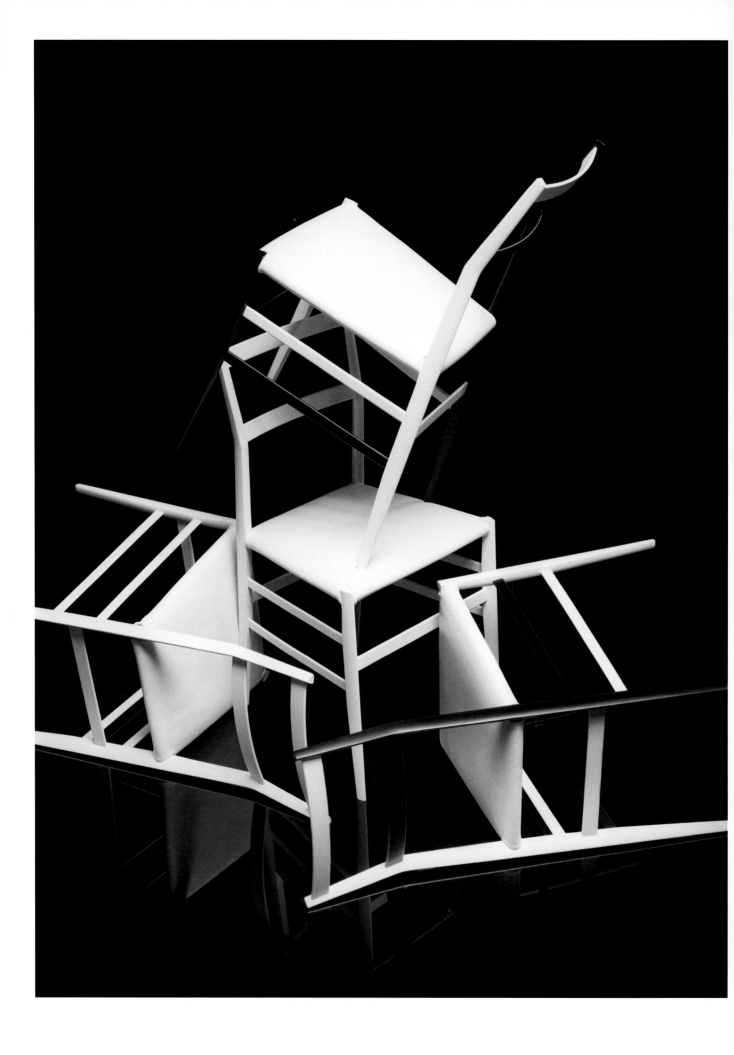

Karl Lagerfeld, fashion designer, publisher and book dealer, began working as a photographer in 1987. Lagerfeld has since received the Lucky Strike Design Award from the Raymond Lewy Foundation, the cultural prize from the German Photographic Society, and the ICP Trustees Award from the International Center of Photography. Steidl has published most of Lagerfeld's books, including Casa Malaparte (1998), A Portrait of Dorian Gray (2004), Room Service (2006), The Beauty of Violence (2010), The Little Black Jacket (2012) and Villa Noailles, Hyères-Été 1995 (2015).

In 2013 the distinguished Italian furniture manufacturing company Cassina invited Karl Lagerfeld to choose his favorite pieces of furniture for an unusual photographic mise-en-scène: "I had never 'worked' on a project like this before. To visually reinterpret examples of perfect design is completely new for me, and therefore stimulating, exciting even."

Before Lagerfeld's lens, iconic chairs, tables and chaise longues by Modernist legends such as Le Corbusier, Rietveld and Perriand condense to their absolute, abstract essence. In his inimitably sleek and sophisticated photographs, Lagerfeld reveals the form in Formalism. Here furniture is seen in an atypical, decontextualized mode of presentation, detached from its usual environment, isolated and dramatically lit like a sculpture. The result is a tenderly chosen compendium of 21 images that respects the artistic intentions of the designers while simultaneously creating a new aesthetic.

Karl Lagerfeld
Cassina as Seen by Karl

Book design by Karl Lagerfeld
and Gerhard Steidl
64 pages
11.4 × 14.6 in. / 29 × 37 cm
21 high-glossy photographs
tipped-in by hand
Four-color process
Clothbound hardcover housed
in a handmade slipcase

€ 85.00 / £ 78.00 / US$ 100.00
ISBN 978-3-86930-738-1

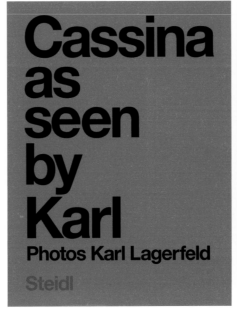

Slipcase

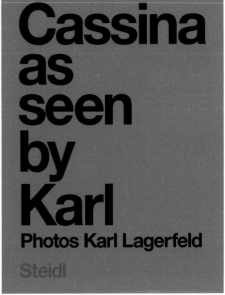

Book

Paulo Nozolino was born in 1955 in Lisbon, and lived in London and Paris before settling again in Portugal. In the span of his 40-year career, Nozolino has traveled widely in Europe, America, the Middle East and North Africa. His work has been largely shown and honored with several awards, and is held in numerous private and public collections. Nozolino's books include Penumbra (Scalo, 1996), Far Cry (Steidl, 2005), bone lonely (Steidl, 2011) and Makulatur (Steidl, 2011).

Taken between 2008 and 2013 in New York, Lisbon, Paris and Berlin as well as in the French and Portuguese countryside, these photographs by Paulo Nozolino bear his usual dark symbolic syntax. Still using 35mm film and occasionally a flash, this tight sequence of vertical pictures shows us, once again, his everlasting concern for the state of the world and his quest for the pure, true, non-manipulated analogic image.

This is a bright obscure piece. The transparency of the black shows a world that is continually destroying itself. Closer to the certitude of an end. The decadence of the place. Life by a thread, leaving traces of light. This is where we came to. This is where we are. All we have left is putrefaction, garbage, claustral confinement, a quiet decay that embraces slow death. So slow that we still may believe it might never come. We see her, we feel her, we touch her with our own hands. Yet. We are responsible for the disease but we don't know how to escape from it. We were hungry and we ate. We are dreaming about the crumbs that we left behind. Unwise. Eyes on the floor, there is no redeeming act. Prisoners of a dirty and corrupted matter. Emptiness. Full of guilt inhabited by a depressing seediness, by careless negligence, by lazy weakness, by the violence of the spirit. Home is a forgotten word. And so are many others. Alexandra Carita

Paulo Nozolino
Loaded Shine

Book design by Paulo Nozolino
and Gerhard Steidl
48 pages
8.04 × 11.7 in. / 21 × 29.7 cm
20 black-and-white photographs
Tritone
Clothbound hardcover

€ 30.00 / £ 25.00 / US$ 35.00
ISBN 978-3-86930-972-9

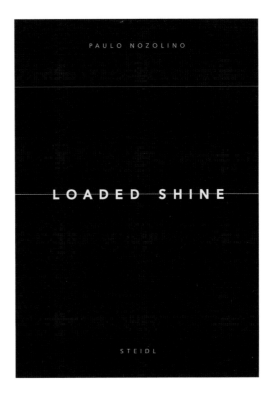

Martine Fougeron was born in Paris in
1954 and studied at Wellesley College and
l'Institut d'Études Politiques de Paris.
For the past 16 years she has lived
with her two sons in New York. After a
successful career as creative director
of a perfumery, Fougeron turned to
photography, studying at the International
Center of Photography in New York. Her
work on her two sons has been exhibited
internationally and is held in major
public and private collections including
the Museum of Fine Arts in Houston,
the Bronx Museum of the Arts and the
Philadelphia Museum of Art. Fougeron is a
regular contributor to The New Yorker and
The New York Times Magazine.

Teen Tribe is a series of intimate portraits of Martine Fougeron's
two adolescent sons and their tribe of friends growing up in New
York and France. Begun in 2005, Fougeron has followed the lives of
her sons Nicolas and Adrien from the ages of thirteen and fourteen
respectively as they entered adulthood. The book pictures adol-
escence as a transformative state, caught between childhood and
adulthood, between the feminine and masculine, between innocence
and burgeoning self-identity. As both mother and photographer,
Fougeron combines a tender transparency for her subject with a more
distanced view of the world of teenagers. *Teen Tribe* is a visual diary
of her sons' domestic lives arranged chronologically, capturing the
different rites of passage and personal challenges they encounter over
time. Inspired by Dutch paintings of domestic scenes, particularly
those of Vermeer, as well as by cinematic compositions, Fougeron's
work is both a sensual biography of two boys, and a depiction of the
universal process of growing up to which all can relate.

Martine Fougeron
Teen Tribe
A World with Two Sons

Essay by Lyle Rexer
Interview by Robert A. Schafer, Jr.
Book design by Martine Fougeron and Gerhard Steidl
144 pages
11 × 9.8 in. / 28 × 25 cm
85 photographs
Four-color process
Hardcover

€ 40.00 / £ 35.00 / US$ 45.00
ISBN 978-3-86930-545-5

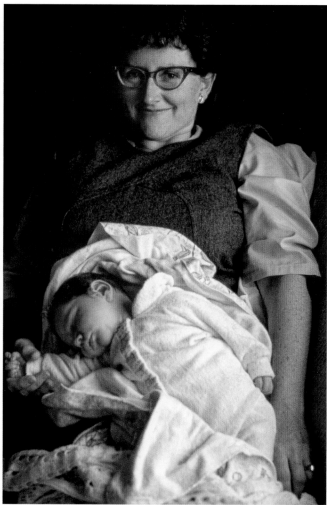

Marq Sutherland, born in San Diego, California, in 1974, grew up in an artistic family. In 1998 he became assistant to contemporary landscape painter Woody Gwen and began his photographic studies with David Scheinbaum and Steve Fitch at the College of Santa Fe, graduating in 2001 with a self-designed Bachelor of Arts in photography, music and technology. He continued his studies with Jack Fulton at the San Francisco Art Institute receiving a Master of Fine Arts in 2005. Sutherland was a finalist for the 2002 Willard Van Dyke Award, and received a SFAI Teaching Assistantship Award in 2004 and a Helen Wurlitzer Foundation Fellowship in 2008. He lives and works in Bilbao, Spain.

Pilgrim is a visual journey into one woman's life through the eyes of her parents, husband and son. In her last years, Marq Sutherland returned home to help his mother through this time during which they spoke about a recurring subject—her past. Years before, Pilgrim had given him his maternal grandfather's and father's photographic negatives. Sifting through thousands of images unseen for decades, Sutherland found many photographs which depicted his mother's life from the moment of birth, and saw how he might complete her story with love and dignity—how they both might hold onto life as they learned to let go.

For me, this book has become both a way to honor the life of my mother, Pilgrim Sutherland, and to connect and collaborate with my grandparents, Poul de Hoffmann and Elsie Boote de Hoffmann, and my father Frank Sutherland through the images they left behind.
Marq Sutherland

Marq Sutherland
Pilgrim

Book design by Marq Sutherland and Gerhard Steidl
Three volumes, 240 pages
5.1 × 8.3 in. / 13 × 21 cm

Vol. 1: Daughter
80 pages
59 photographs

Vol. 2: Wife
80 pages
51 photographs

Vol. 3: Mother
80 pages
66 photographs

Four-color process
Three softcover books housed in a slipcase

€ 48.00 / £ 45.00 / US$ 65.00
ISBN 978-3-86930-695-7

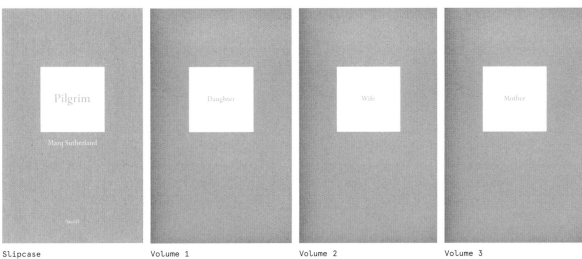

Slipcase   Volume 1   Volume 2   Volume 3

Jan Jedlička was born in Prague in 1944, where he studied painting at the academy before immigrating to Switzerland in 1969. He turned to photography rather late in his career. Jedlička's work has been exhibited at museums and galleries throughout Europe, including Kunstmuseum and Kunsthalle Winterthur, the National Gallery of Prague, CAMeC La Spezia, and the Josef Albers Museum, Bottrop. Steidl published his Il Cerchio / The Circle in 2008. Jedlička has had a long connection with Italy, and lives in Zurich and Prague.

While working on his book *The Circle* in 2005, focusing on the capricious Maremma area in Southern Tuscany, Jan Jedlička came across a short coastal strip of immense diversity at Principina a Mare near Grosseto. The constant atmospheric transformations of its landscape under the spell of the sky's play of light instantly caught his attention and inspired him to return frequently between 2008 and the summer of 2015. Jedlička visited this tiny spot by the sea in all seasons and weather conditions, capturing images of vivid summer beach life, deserted parking lots and surreal wetlands bulging with abstract formations and vegetation between the water and the dunes. The black-and-white images were all taken in the range of only 200 meters, suggesting that we can discover a huge variety of spectacular natural phenomena in our most immediate environments.

Jedlička is fascinated by the continuous change of the phenomena in front of our eyes, forming newly at any moment. Heinz Liesbrock

Jan Jedlička
200 m

Texts by Jan Jedlička and Urs Stahel
Book design by Trix Wetter
156 pages
11.6 × 10.8 in. / 29.5 × 27.5 cm
65 black-and-white photographs
Tritone
Clothbound hardcover with a tipped-in photograph

€ 48.00 / £ 45.00 / US$ 55.00
ISBN 978-3-95829-101-0

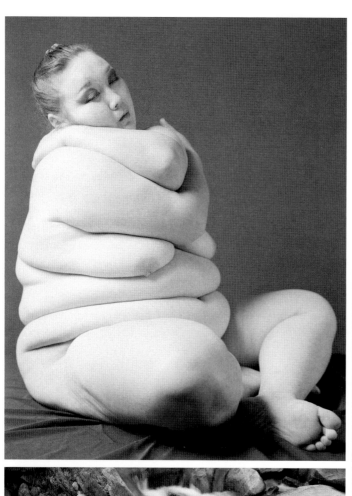

124

Liu Zheng was born in Wuqiang Province, China in 1969 and grew up in a mining district of Shanxi Province. He studied in the Engineering and Optics Department of the Beijing Institute of Technology, and in 1995 co-founded the journal New Photography. Between 1994 and 2001 Liu Zheng traveled extensively throughout China to produce his series The Chinese. Outside China his work has been shown in France, Italy and New York.

The "dream shock" of Liu Zheng's title refers to an awakening as if from a deep sleep. There is a moment between sleep and consciousness in which the dream state and conscious reality collide. It is a fertile, erotic and sometimes violent area of the mind, in which both exquisite and tortured imagery may surface.

Liu Zheng is one of the few Chinese photographers whose work has reached the West. The exhibition of his extensive series "The Chinese" at ICP in New York in 2004 and the accompanying Steidl book indicated he was working on the borders between the documentary tradition and the extended portrait school of August Sander. His background with the *Workers' Daily* suggests his grounding as a photojournalist. Yet Liu Zheng's vision does not echo the common view of China, characterized by anonymity in the sheer mass of the population or by the momentum of industry. Frequently the subjects of his portraits are those on the fringes of Chinese society; his outsiders contribute to an unfamiliar collective portrait of a nation.

Dream Shock brings us to another space that exists in the mind itself. Some of the characters, such as a beautiful Peking Opera singer, may be half-familiar, but the historical references to a brutal occupation and the sexual explicitness take us into unprecedented territory. Elaborate scenes are delicately choreographed in a series of terrifying tableaux. The directness of photographic evidence exists alongside studio staging that is pure and unsettling theatre. We enter a wholly new domain.

Liu Zheng has eclipsed all the previous photographic clichés of the Chinese people and Chinese culture. Liu's photography is like a window opening onto a grand view of the cruelty and the darkness of this culture. Gu Zheng

Liu Zheng
Dream Shock

Edited by Mark Holborn
Introduction by Mark Holborn
Book design by Jesse Holborn
108 pages
11.5 × 12.1 in. / 29.2 × 30.8 cm
60 black-and-white photographs
Tritone
Clothbound hardcover with a tipped-in photograph

€ 40.00 / £ 35.00 / US$ 45.00
ISBN 978-3-95829-267-3

Born in New York in 1956, Jerry Spagnoli
is one of the principal practitioners of
the daguerreotype and lectures regularly
on the subject. His work is held in the
collections of the Whitney Museum of
American Art in New York, the Museum of
Fine Arts in Boston and the National
Portrait Gallery in Washington D.C.
Spagnoli's work has appeared in many
publications, and Steidl has released
his Daguerreotypes (2006) and American
Dreaming (2011).

Between May and September 2012, Jerry Spagnoli photographed the myriad faces of people transfixed by an enormous electronic billboard above New York's Times Square. *Regard*, the result of this ambitious documentary undertaking, is a visual chronicle presenting almost 500 faces of great cultural and individual diversity.

The particular billboard in question was set up to periodically display an image of the crowd beneath it. Pedestrians would wander by, absorbed in their thoughts, before noticing the billboard and pausing to search for their images. On finding themselves, many marked the occasion with an obligatory selfie. Spagnoli recorded these processes and the emotions of expectation and delight they elicit, creating an intricate collective portrait.

For me the situation was compelling and complex. The light in Times Square is particularly beautiful at that time of the year. The expressions on people's faces were open and unselfconscious, as they all looked up towards that great light in the sky. Jerry Spagnoli

Jerry Spagnoli
Regard

Book design by Jerry Spagnoli
936 pages
5.9 × 7.9 in. / 15 × 20 cm
467 color photographs
Four-color process
Clothbound hardcover with a tipped-in photograph

€ 68.00 / £ 64.00 / US$ 75.00
ISBN 978-3-95829-239-0

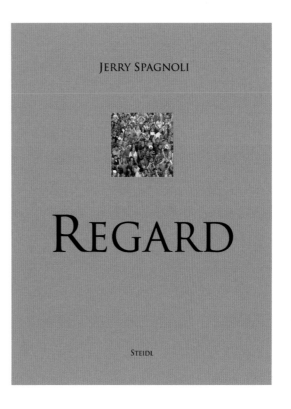

Soweto

Dukathole

Johannesburg

Santu Mofokeng was born in Johannesburg
in 1956. After working as a darkroom
assistant for various newspapers,
he joined Afrapix, a collective of
photographers dedicated to the struggle
against apartheid. His interest in
depicting ordinary township life, however,
led him to work for the African Studies
Institute at Wits University from 1988
until 1998. Over the past three decades,
Mofokeng has created an exceptional,
open-ended body of work that probes the
meaning and authority of photography
while subverting stereotypical notions
of the black South African experience.
In 2011 a retrospective of Mofokeng's
work opened at the Jeu de Paume in Paris
before traveling internationally, and in
2013 he represented Germany at the Venice
Biennale.

Santu Mofokeng began to dedicate himself to portraying everyday
experience in South African townships in 1985, first as a member of
the Afrapix collective, and then as a documentary photographer for
the African Studies Institute at the University of the Witwatersrand.
This set of publications, which continues a groundbreaking reappraisal
of the photographer's archive, presents aspects of life in Soweto,
where Mofokeng grew up; Dukathole, a township in the East Rand of
Gauteng Province; and Johannesburg, the city in which he worked.
Taken together, they invite a nuanced understanding of largely unsung
narratives from a crucial period in South African history which saw the
demise of apartheid.

*Mr. Mofokeng produced some of the great pictures of the apartheid
years, but his images were different from many others of the time.
His interest was less in a photojournalistic documenting of battles
between South African blacks and the repressive government, than
in recording the dynamics of another front line: daily life in black
communities.* Holland Cotter, *The New York Times*

Santu Mofokeng
Stories 5–7
Soweto—Dukathole—Johannesburg

Edited by Santu Mofokeng and Joshua Chuang
Book design by Victor Balko
9.5 x 12.6 in. / 24 x 32 cm

Book 5: Soweto
36 pages
35 black-and-white photographs

Book 6: Dukathole
44 pages
31 black-and-white photographs

Book 7: Johannesburg
32 pages
22 black-and-white photographs

Quadratone
Three sewn softcover booklets in a
cardboard envelope

€ 50.00 / £ 45.00 / US$ 55.00
ISBN 978-3-95829-277-2

Envelope and books 5–7

Born in 1971 in Meudon outside Paris, Karine Laval today lives and works in Brooklyn, New York. Her work has been widely exhibited at venues including the Palm Springs Art Museum, Los Angeles Center for Digital Art, Sørlandets Art Museum in Kristiansand, Palais de Tokyo in Paris, and photography festivals throughout Europe and the US. Laval has been recognized with the Peter S. Reed Foundation Grant, and as one of the Humble Art Foundation's 31 Women in Art Photography (2011), Photo District News' 30 for New and Emerging Photographers (2005), and the Magenta Foundation's Emerging Photographers of the Year (2005 and 2009). Laval was nominated for the Prix Pictet in 2016.

Poolscapes brings together two connected bodies of work—"The Pool" (2002–05) and "Poolscapes" (2009–12)—focused on the motif of the swimming pool and realized over the course of ten years. Presenting public pools in urban and natural environments throughout Europe and private pools in the US in two distinct sections, the book is arranged chronologically and shows an evolution in tone and depth, from the real to the imagined, from the photographic to the painterly.

Poolscapes opens with the "The Pool" series which invites us into a sun-bleached public pool at midday, evocative of playful, mundane childhood memories and the universal experience of leisure and bathing. Gradually these geometric lines and familiar architectural structures with their social and descriptive references give way to the abstract, often blurred shapes and colors of the "Poolscapes" pictures that oscillate between representation and abstraction. Here the pool becomes a metaphor, a mirror whose surface reflects the surrounding world but is also a gate into a submerged realm where bathers are distorted and fragmented—"murky waters" that reveal the unconscious and darker connotations of the pool.

Laval's photographs rely on casual collisions and are at once vibrant, witty and spontaneous. Recording the world but transforming it at the same time, they find an extreme beauty in the banal and, by the same token, celebrate life and its more idle pleasures. Tim Clark, *Next Level*

Karine Laval
Poolscapes

Text by Claire Barliant
Book design by Karine Laval and Gerhard Steidl
128 pages
9.4 x 12.6 in. / 24 x 32 cm
70 color photographs
Four-color process
Clothbound hardcover

€ 42.00 / £ 35.00 / US$ 48.00
ISBN 978-3-95829-261-1

Ed Kashi is a photojournalist, filmmaker, speaker and educator. A member of VII Photo Agency, Kashi is recognized for his complex imagery and compelling rendering of the human condition. Along with numerous awards, including Pictures of the Year International Multimedia Photographer of the Year 2015, Kashi's photos have been published and exhibited worldwide, and have generated eight books, including Sugar Cane / Syrian Refugees published by Steidl in 2016.

If Cartier-Bresson's "decisive moment" reflects a situation perfectly in tune with the photographer's intuition, flawlessly combining the elements of composition and timing, then Ed Kashi's "abandoned moment" is the result of an imprecise instant of surrender. The photos in this book are moving glimpses of transitory events filled with an untamed, frenetic energy—the perfect chaos of everyday life.

For nearly 40 years, Kashi has photographed the instantaneous imperfections that define his abandoned moment. Seeking to reconcile the dichotomy that many people like to look at photos but do not want to be photographed, Kashi stumbled upon a method of uncontrolled photographic observation while still a young practioner. In contrast to his journalistic approach of personally connecting with his subject, keenly observing visual elements and going in-depth, in *Abandoned Moments* Kashi employs geometry, mood and emotion to capture spontaneous experiences with a touch of the mysterious and sometimes fictional.

Ed Kashi is intelligent, brave and compassionate. He always under-stands the nuances of his subjects. He fearlessly goes where few would venture. And he sympathetically captures the soul of each situation. Ed is one of the best of a new breed of photojournalistic artists.
David Griffin, former director of photography at *National Geographic*

Ed Kashi
Abandoned Moments

Edited by Jennifer Larsen, Marjorie Steffe and Mallika Vora
Foreword by Alison Nordstrom
Book design by Mallika Vora
128 pages
11 × 8.5 in. / 27.9 × 21.6 cm
26 black-and-white and 42 color photographs
Four-color process
Clothbound hardcover

€ 35.00 / £ 30.00 / US$ 40.00
ISBN 978-3-95829-274-1

Koto Bolofo was born in South Africa in 1959 and raised in Great Britain. Bolofo has photographed for magazines such as Vogue, Vanity Fair and GQ, and made short films for the Berlinale and the Venice Film Festival. He has created advertising campaigns for companies including Hermès, Christian Dior, Louis Vuitton and Dom Pérignon. Bolofo's books with Steidl include Venus (2008), Horse Power (2010), I Spy with My Little Eye, Something Beginning with S (2010), Vroom! Vroom! (2010), La Maison (2011) and The Prison (2014).

Hahnemühle is the oldest paper mill in Germany—and indeed the world—which has consistently produced fine art paper since its inception over 400 years ago. Using their own supply of spring water and imported pulps, Hahnemühle crafts luxury papers based on time-tested traditional methods. In *Paper Making*, Koto Bolofo graphically captures Hahnemühle's artisanal processes and antique machinery alongside today's most advanced technologies, uncovering the attention to detail, vision and pride that have sustained the company's unmatched reputation for centuries.

Koto Bolofo
Paper Making

Texts by Koto Bolofo
and Gerhard Steidl
Book design by Koto Bolofo
and Gerhard Steidl
160 pages
11.4 × 14.6 in. / 29 × 37 cm
148 black-and-white photographs
Quadratone
Clothbound hardcover

€ 45.00 / £ 40.00 / US$ 50.00
ISBN 978-3-86930-637-7

Koto Bolofo was born in South Africa in 1959 and raised in Great Britain. Bolofo has photographed for magazines such as Vogue, Vanity Fair and GQ, and made short films for the Berlinale and the Venice Film Festival. He has created advertising campaigns for companies including Hermès, Christian Dior, Louis Vuitton and Dom Pérignon. Bolofo's books with Steidl include Venus (2008), Horse Power (2010), I Spy with My Little Eye, Something Beginning with S (2010), Vroom! Vroom! (2010), La Maison (2011) and The Prison (2014).

This whimsical and in-depth behind-the-scenes study leads the reader into the world of Steidl Publishers in Göttingen. With his inimitable and patient eye, Koto Bolofo takes us through the labyrinthine corridors and stairways of the publishing house, documenting the myriad processes and people at work, and giving us an insider's glance into how Steidl's books come to life.

Koto Bolofo
Printing

Text by Koto Bolofo
Book design by Koto Bolofo
and Gerhard Steidl
With a video by Koto Bolofo on DVD
80 pages
11.4 × 12.6 in. / 29 × 37 cm
130 color photographs
Four-color process
Clothbound hardcover

€ 45.00 / £ 40.00 / US$ 50.00
ISBN 978-3-86930-636-0

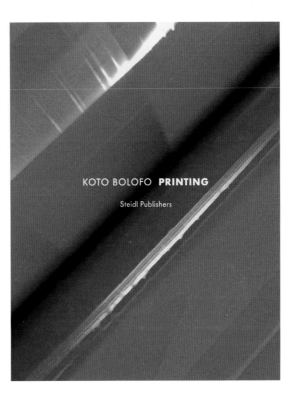

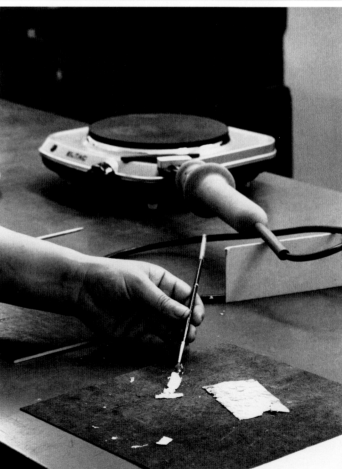

Koto Bolofo was born in South Africa in 1959 and raised in Great Britain. Bolofo has photographed for magazines such as Vogue, Vanity Fair and GQ, and made short films for the Berlinale and the Venice Film Festival. He has created advertising campaigns for companies including Hermès, Christian Dior, Louis Vuitton and Dom Pérignon. Bolofo's books with Steidl include Venus (2008), Horse Power (2010), I Spy with My Little Eye, Something Beginning with S (2010), Vroom! Vroom! (2010), La Maison (2011) and The Prison (2014).

Koto Bolofo creases book spines and gently flicks through pages to explore what has happened behind the scenes in the world of bookbinding—an ancient craft that has protected our most valuable manuscripts since the infancy of art and literature, keeping safe the wisdom of the past. As the processes of binding have now increasingly moved from man to machine, Bolofo's *Binding* is a meticulous study of bookbinding today that embraces the new and laments the loss of the old. The human touch is still evident, but is gradually disappearing. Trying to hold back the tides of time, Bolofo playfully begs the question: has this cherished practice lost its soul and are we now slaves to the machine?

To bind books is to do the impossible. Koto Bolofo

Koto Bolofo
Binding

Text by Koto Bolofo
Book design by Koto Bolofo
and Gerhard Steidl
80 pages
11.4 × 12.6 in. / 29 × 37 cm
80 photographs
Quadratone
Clothbound hardcover

€ 45.00 / £ 40.00 / US$ 50.00
ISBN 978-3-86930-635-3

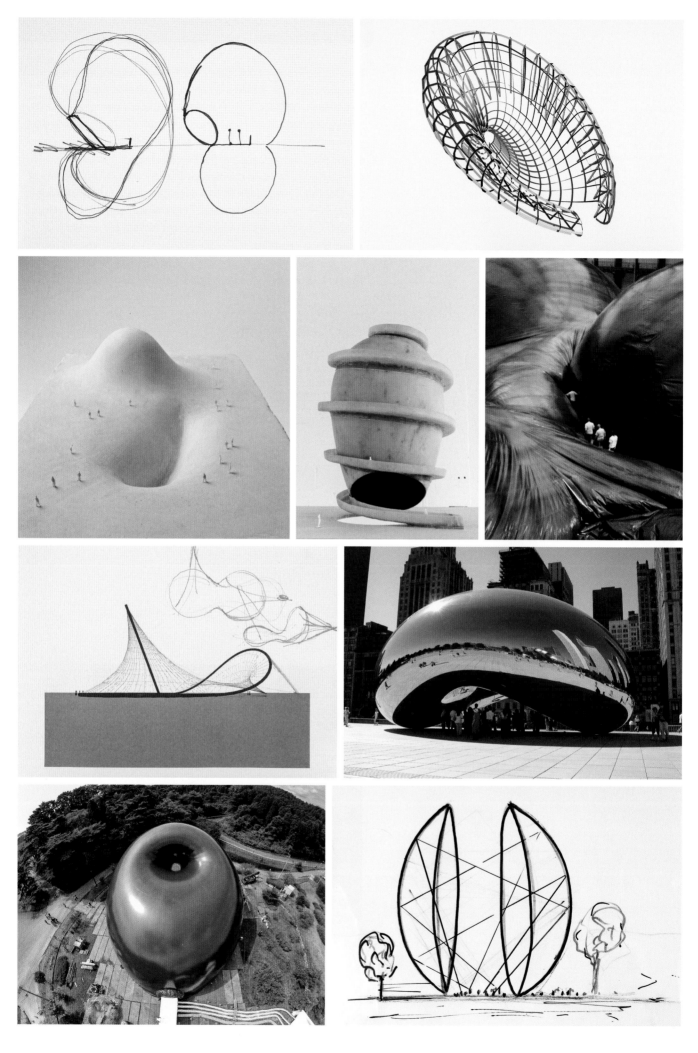

Anish Kapoor was born in 1954 in Mumbai.
Between 1973 and 1978 he studied Fine Art
at Hornsey College of Art, then at the
Chelsea School of Art. Kapoor represented
Britain at the 44th Venice Biennale
and won the Turner Prize in 1991. Solo
exhibitions and public commissions
include Tate Modern (2002); Royal Academy
(2009); Cloud Gate, Millennium Park,
Chicago (2004); Grand Palais, Paris
(2011); Orbit, Olympic Park (2012);
Martin-Gropius-Bau (2013) and Chateau du
Versailles (2015). Kapoor lives and works
in London.

This publication brings together for the first time Anish Kapoor's architectural projects and ideas that span the last 40 years. These are concepts that continue to inform all areas of Kapoor's artistic output, many of which have been realized in works that confound the distinctions between art and architecture, pushing architecture into radical new territory.

Kapoor's projects renegotiate the relationship not only between art and architecture but also between the very sense of space within ourselves and that of the external world. The forms he presents to us create spaces that blur the duality of subject and object, of interior and exterior. Monochrome fields of color, mirrored surfaces and fathomless voids all destabilize our place in the world. The more than 2,000 sketches, models, renderings and plans in this book show the journey of these forms to how they might exist in reality as well as the spaces they inhabit or create, both outside and within us.

For a long time before—even from the pigment pieces—I'd been thinking of my work as potential architecture. I've always been convinced by the idea that to make new art you have to make new space.
Anish Kapoor

Anish Kapoor
Make New Space
Architectural Projects

Edited by Anish Kapoor Studio
Book design by Brighten the Corners
6.9 × 9.4 in. / 17.5 × 24 cm
Vol. 1
600 pages
1,053 color photographs and images
Vol. 2
592 pages
1,053 color photographs and images
Four-color process
Two otabind softcovers in a sleeve

€ 100.00 / £ 95.00 / US$ 125.00
ISBN 978-3-95829-420-2

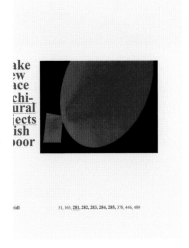

Anish Kapoor was born in 1954 in Mumbai. Between 1973 and '78 he studied Fine Art at Hornsey College of Art, then at the Chelsea School of Art. He represented Britain at the 44th Venice Biennale and won the Turner Prize in 1991. Solo exhibitions and public commissions include Tate Modern (2002); Royal Academy (2009); Cloud Gate, Millennium Park, Chicago (2004); Grand Palais, Paris (2011); Orbit, Olympic Park (2012); Martin-Gropius-Bau (2013) and Chateau du Versailles (2015). Kapoor lives and works in London.

The powerful religious sites of Uluru and Kata Tjuta in the Northern Territory of Australia have been of deep interest to the artist Anish Kapoor since he first visited them in the 1980s. At Uluru he found a landscape of monumental scale which contained intimate and ritually resonant sites. A landscape of hollows and voids which he has read as resonant of primal or even "original" structure. Kapoor describes Uluru as "an object with a perforated skin which lends itself to mythic meaning."

On his visit in 1991, Kapoor noted in his sketchbook "a white bump on a white wall." He later made the sculpture *When I am Pregnant* (1992), describing it as "an object in a state of becoming." The idea of the proto-object is central to Kapoor's work. In 2012 Kapoor returned to Uluru and Kata Tjuta. These two photographic volumes trace his journey. They reveal through his eyes the artist's pre-occupation with form and pre-form, skin and surface in relation to deep interior.

Unbelievable things revealed themselves every day. I felt deeply connected with the place, and with a kind of possible interpretation, a symbolic interpretation of the holes and the strips of stone that seem to be leaning against it. I was amazed, not at the monolith, but at the way the monolith seemed to be made up of symbolic events.
Anish Kapoor

Anish Kapoor
Uluru & Kata Tjuta Photographs

Edited by Anish Kapoor Studio
Book design by Brighten the Corners
5.5 × 8.1 in. / 14 × 20.5 cm

Vol. 1: Uluru
584 pages
278 color photographs

Vol. 2: Kata Tjuta
168 pages
84 color photographs

Four-color process
Two otabind softcovers in a slipcase

€ 78.00 / £ 68.00 / US$ 85.00
ISBN 978-3-95829-260-4

Slipcase

Volume 1: Uluru

Volume 2: Kata Tjuta

Arthur Elgort, born in 1940 in New York City, has photographed the world's most beautiful and talented people for over forty years. He has published seven books to date including Personal Fashion (1983), The Swan Prince (1987), Models Manual (1993) and Camera Ready (1997). In addition to Ballet, Edition 7L has published Camera Crazy (2004) and The Big Picture (2014).

Following his career-spanning monograph *The Big Picture*, Arthur Elgort pays homage to his first love and eternal muse in this new collection of photographs. While glimpsing ballet through Elgort's lens we are taken not to the front of the stage but behind the scenes, where the hard work is done. On this journey through the hallways and rehearsal spaces of some of the world's most distinguished ballet schools, including the New York City Ballet and the Vaganova Academy of Russian Ballet, we see previously unpublished images of legends such as Balanchine, Baryshnikov and Lopatkina. The perfection of the prima ballerina disappears in these quiet photographs where the viewer is able to witness the individual dancers' natural glamor as they work to perfect their craft. Elgort's snapshot style allows the pain and pleasure of one of the world's most beloved forms of expressive dance to be seen with beauty.

From the first day I worked with Arthur I realized his prism is dance. He took its languid, exuberant perfection as his inspiration when he found himself a young Turk in fashion photography. It has to this day served as his anchor. Christiaan

Arthur Elgort
Ballet

Book design by Marianne Houtenbos
168 pages
9.5 × 11.8 in. / 24 × 30 cm
114 black-and-white and color photographs
Four-color process
Hardcover

€ 45.00 / £ 40.00 / US$ 50.00
ISBN 978-3-95829-191-1

Edition 7L Paris

Lucinda Devlin, born in Ann Arbor, Michigan, in 1947, grew up surrounded by the Great Lakes and rural landscapes. Devlin has received numerous awards (including those from the NEA and DAAD) and her work is held in several museums, such as the Guggenheim Museum, the Whitney Museum, and the DZ Bank Collection. Devlin has exhibited throughout the United States and Europe including at the Venice Biennale. Steidl has published her The Omega Suites (2000) and Water Rites (2003).

Lake Pictures is a series of photographs of Lake Huron, one of the Great Lakes bordering the state of Michigan. The pictures — taken at the same place, during the four seasons, and at different times of day and night — explore the changing atmospheric nature of the lake through the prisms of water, sky, color, light, place, space and time. Looking at this immense body of water and the sky above, both initially seem boundless, as if stretching forever into the distance. Only the fine horizon line between the two separates and joins them, pulling us into each photo and reminding us that this sense of infinity is but an intriguing optical fiction.

More than a lake: the *lake, the sea. Devlin's pictures show everything, from a honey-yellow pool to a raging sea; we see the grayish-brown abyss, the opaque, rippling navy blue, a melancholy carpet ... and the slate-like idleness. All this is a result of her morning, midday, evening and nighttime visits to the shoreline. It looks as though the photographer has consulted the Great Lake like an oracle.*
Ulf Erdmann Ziegler

Co-published with Galerie m Bochum

Lucinda Devlin
Lake Pictures

Text by Jerry Dennis and Tom Sherman
Book design by Gerhard Steidl
120 pages
11.2 × 10 in. / 28.5 × 25.5 cm
50 color photographs
Four-color process
Hardcover

€ 38.00 / £ 35.00 / US$ 40.00
ISBN 978-3-86930-965-1

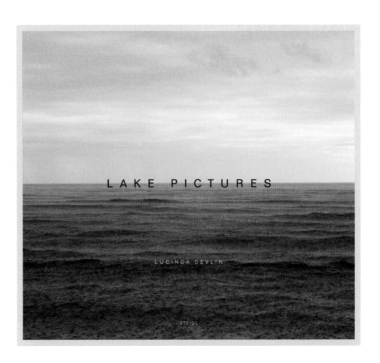

Hannah Collins was born in London in 1956. From 1989 to 2010 she lived and worked in Barcelona, and today lives between London and Almeria, Spain. Collins has received many awards including a Fulbright Scholarship and was nominated for the Turner Prize in 1993. In 2015 a retrospective of her work was shown at the Sprengel Museum Hannover, in conjunction with the award of the Spectrum Prize. In addition to the Hannover retrospective publication, Collins' last book was The Fragile Feast (2011). She has completed a recent body of work in Japan and has ongoing projects in Amazonia and the American South.

Noah Purifoy (1917-2004) moved to Los Angeles in 1953 and enrolled as the first African-American student at what is now the California Institute of the Arts. Purifoy graduated with a BFA just before his fortieth birthday. With fellow artist Judson Powell he organized the exhibition "66 Signs of Neon" with material salvaged from the Watts Rebellion. He co-founded the Watts Towers Arts Center, and initiated various programs to bring art into the prison system. The Noah Purifoy Outdoor Sculpture Museum is situated near Joshua Tree in the Mojave Desert.

Hannah Collins
Noah Purifoy

Edited with Mark Holborn
Text by Hannah Collins
Book design by Hannah Collins (following Walker Evans' book Message from the Interior)
44 pages
13.8 × 14.5 in. / 35 × 36.7 cm
18 black-and-white photographs
Tritone
Clothbound hardcover

€ 78.00 / £ 70.00 / US$ 85.00
ISBN 978-3-95829-268-0

Though born in Snow Hill, Alabama in 1917, Noah Purifoy lived most of his life in Los Angeles and Joshua Tree, California, where he died in 2004. The exhibition of his work, *Junk Dada*, at LACMA in 2015 as well as the recent publication by Steidl of his notebooks and essays in *High Desert,* have contributed to the legacy of this long-overlooked artist who first came to prominence with sculpture assembled from the debris of the Watts Rebellion of 1965.

In the last 15 years of his life Purifoy lived in the Mojave Desert where he created large-scale sculptures spread over ten acres. On visiting this site Hannah Collins made a series of exquisite black-and-white photographic studies of Purifoy's work. Her rigorous aesthetic stance is unwittingly reminiscent of the formality of Walker Evans, who would have greatly appreciated Purifoy's transformation of discarded materials into grand yet vernacular forms.

Message from the Interior, Walker Evans' photographic study of 1966, which through the selection of a handful of pictures of interiors suggests a wide and disparate landscape, became a model for the publication of Collins' work from Purifoy's site. Her 18 photographs are presented here in a format that exactly echoes Evans' publication, both typographically and spatially. The intention is not imitative, but refers to the grandeur and scale achieved by Purifoy. Cumulatively his work becomes a transitory monument inevitably destined to decay into the desert itself.

I do not wish to be an artist. I only wish that art enables me to be.
Noah Purifoy

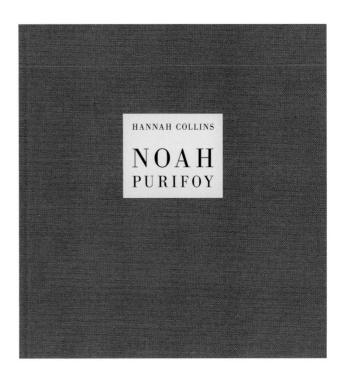

Harry Callahan (1912-99) began his career as an amateur photographer. Following a workshop with Ansel Adams in 1941 and a meeting with Alfred Stieglitz in 1942, Callahan decided to completely devote himself to the medium. In 1946 he accepted László Moholy-Nagy's invitation to teach at Chicago's Institute of Design, a position he left in 1961 to chair the Photography Department at the Rhode Island School of Design. Since his first one-person show in 1947, Callahan's work has been the subject of over 60 solo and group exhibitions worldwide, 18 of which were presented at The Museum of Modern Art, New York.

One of the foremost American photographers of the twentieth century, Harry Callahan explored the expressive possibilities of both color and black-and-white photography from the outset of his career in 1938. Following his retirement from teaching at the Rhode Island School of Design in 1977, however, he decided to dedicate his practice exclusively to the color medium and pursue travel to foreign locales.

The 23 photographs in this publication, taken in Morocco in 1981, are the product of Callahan's shift to a strictly chromatic palette and demonstrate his continued interest in the visual intrigue of the every-day urban landscape and the passersby who occupy it. Depicting his familiar subjects of architectural facades, random patterns of street activity, and isolated figures lost in thought, the images transcend Morocco's exoticism by exploring the formal and pictorial potential of the country's environment.

The photographs that excite me are photographs that say something in a new manner; not for the sake of being different, but ones that are different because the individual is different and the individual expresses himself. Harry Callahan

Co-published with Pace/MacGill Gallery, New York

Harry Callahan
Morocco

Book design by Steidl Design
56 pages
11.7 × 9.1 in. / 29.7 × 23 cm
23 color photographs
Four-color process
Clothbound hardcover

€ 38.00 / £ 30.00 / US$ 40.00
ISBN 978-3-95829-166-9

STEIDL PACE/MACGILL

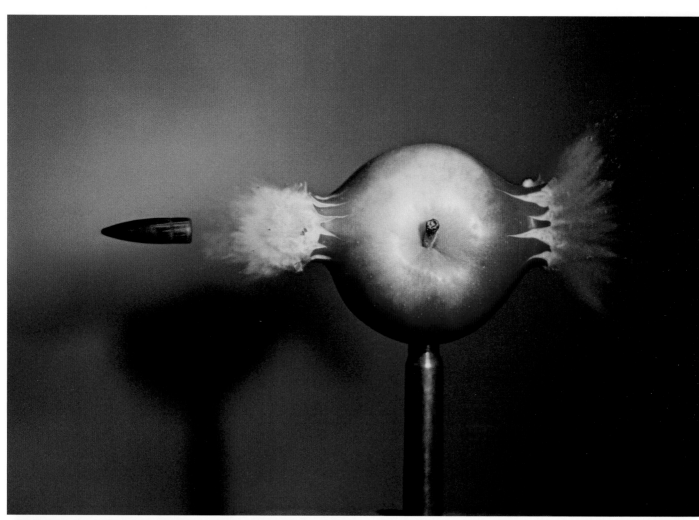

As Harold Eugene Edgerton (1903-90) simply said: "I am an electrical engineer and I work with strobe lights and circuits and make useful things." Born and raised in Nebraska, the longtime Massachusetts Institute of Technology electrical engineering professor pioneered the transformation of the strobe from an obscure nineteenth-century invention into a key technology of the twentieth century.

Harold Edgerton was an engineer, educator, explorer, entrepreneur, as well as a revolutionary photographer—in the words of his former student and *Life* photographer Gjon Mili, "an American original." Edgerton's photos combine exceptional engineering talent with aesthetic sensibility, and this book presents more than 100 of his most exemplary works.

Seeing the Unseen contains iconic photos from the beloved milk drops and bullets slicing through fruit and cards, to less well known but equally compelling images of sea creatures and sports figures in action. Paired with excerpts from Edgerton's laboratory notebooks, the book reveals the full range of his technical virtuosity and his enthusiasm for the natural and human-built worlds. Essays by Edgerton students and collaborators J. Kim Vandiver and Gus Kayafas explore his approach to photography, engineering and education, while MIT Museum curators Gary Van Zante and Deborah Douglas examine his significance to the history of photography, technology and modern culture.

In many ways, unexpected results are what have most inspired my photography. Harold Edgerton

Co-published with the MIT Museum, Cambridge, Massachusetts

Harold Edgerton
Seeing the Unseen

Edited by Ron Kurtz, Deborah Douglas and Gus Kayafas
Texts by Ron Kurtz, J. Kim Vandiver, Gus Kayafas, Gary Van Zante and Deborah Douglas
Book design by Holger Feroudj and Gerhard Steidl
224 pages
8.8 x 11.2 in. / 22.5 x 28.5 cm
115 black-and-white and 43 color images
Four-color process
Clothbound hardcover with a dust jacket

€ 48.00 / £ 44.00 / US$ 50.00
ISBN 978-3-95829-308-3

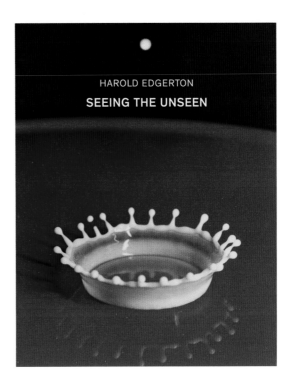

Born in 1922 in Marburg, Evelyn Hofer grew up in Switzerland and Spain. She completed photographic apprenticeships in Basel and Zurich before studying under Hans Finsler, and in 1946 settled in New York. Hofer's career took a decisive turn with her photos for Mary McCarthy's The Stones of Florence (1959); books on London, Spain, New York, Washington and Dublin followed, as well as Emerson in Italy (1989). In the 1970s Hofer focused on society-related subjects and published photo-essays in Life and the New York Times Magazine. She also photographed public figures, interiors for magazines, and in later life primarily personal subjects. Hofer died in Mexico City in 2009.

The starting point for Evelyn Hofer's *New York* is the 1965 book *New York Proclaimed*, which features an in-depth essay by V. S. Pritchett and photos by Hofer, and enjoyed great popularity upon its original publication. *New York Proclaimed* is an example of Hofer's perhaps most important body of work, her city portraits: books that present comprehensive prose texts by renowned authors alongside her self-contained visual essays with their own narratives. The newly conceived *New York* focuses on Hofer's photos of the 1960s as well as until now unpublished images from the early 1970s.

In Hofer's photos of the street and (semi-)public spaces, people and architecture become symbols of a particular time and place. She immersed herself in New York society and captured these aspects of the everyday—inconspicuous and subtle, yet all the more enduring for being so—in images that invariably reflect the zeitgeist. *New York* contains a new essay by John Haskell which posits possible stories behind Hofer's photos and draws connections between images taken over the course of ten years.

In reality everything that we photographers photograph is ourselves in the other. Evelyn Hofer

Evelyn Hofer
New York

Edited by Andreas Pauly and Sabine Schmid
Text by John Haskell
Book design by Holger Feroudj
144 pages
8.7 × 11.2 in. / 21.5 × 28 cm
64 black-and-white and 26 color photographs
Tritone and four-color process
Clothbound hardcover with a tipped-in photograph

€ 45.00 / £ 40.00 / US$ 50.00
ISBN 978-3-95829-348-9

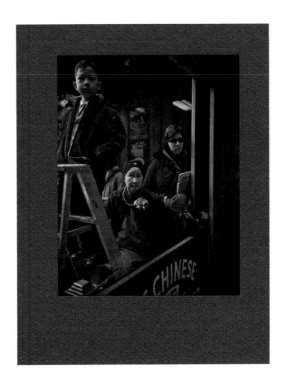

Ernest Cole was born near Pretoria in 1940. Leaving school at 17 to become a photographer, he secured staff jobs and freelance assignments for newspapers and magazines for blacks—honing his skills with a correspondence course from the New York Institute of Photography. Inspired by Henri Cartier-Bresson's book The People of Moscow, in 1960 Cole embarked on a project to document the lives of his people which resulted in House of Bondage.

First published in the United States in 1967 and in Britain in 1968, *House of Bondage* presented images from South Africa that shocked the world. The young African photographer had left his country at 26 to find an audience for his stunning exposure of the system of racial dominance known as apartheid. In 185 photographs, Cole's book showed from the vantage point of the oppressed how the system closely regulated and controlled the lives of the black majority. He saw every aspect of this oppression with a searching eye and a passionate heart.

House of Bondage is a milestone in the history of documentary photography, even though it was immediately banned in South Africa. In a *Chicago Tribune* review of 1967 Robert Cromie described it as "one of the frankest books ever done on South Africa—with photographs by a native of that country who would be most unwise to attempt to return for some years." Cole died in exile in 1990 as the regime was collapsing, never knowing when his portrait of his homeland would finally find its way home. Not until the Apartheid Museum in Johannesburg mounted enlarged pages of the book on its walls in 2001 were his people able to view these pictures, which are as powerful and provocative today as they were 50 years ago.

Ernest Cole's photographs are important because they relieve the tedium and go beyond precepts. They are the raw facts of the matter, not just images of injustice. Joseph Lelyveld

Ernest Cole
House of Bondage

Texts by Thomas Flaherty and Joseph Lelyveld
Book design by Steidl Design
192 pages
8.3 x 11.4 in. / 21 x 29 cm
185 black-and-white photographs
Tritone
Clothbound hardcover with dust jacket

€ 58.00 / £ 54.00 / US$ 60.00
ISBN 978-3-95829-346-5

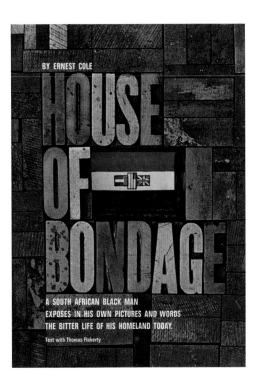

Lewis Baltz was born in Newport Beach, California, in 1945, where he grew up. He graduated from the San Francisco Art Institute in 1969 and received a Master's degree from Claremont Graduate School in 1971. Apart from the definitive exhibition "New Topographics: Photographs of a Man-Altered Landscape," Baltz's work has been shown in about 50 solo exhibitions and featured in 17 monographs. It now forms part of the permanent collections of the Guggenheim Museum, Tate Modern, the Los Angeles County Museum of Art and the San Francisco Museum of Modern Art, to name but a few. In 2013, Baltz donated his archive to the Getty Research Institute. He lived, taught and photographed in Europe from the mid-1980s, splitting his time between Paris and Venice. Baltz died in Paris on November 22, 2014, aged 69.

In the late 1960s and early '70s Lewis Baltz became fascinated by the stark, repellent, manmade landscape that was rolling over California's then still agrarian terrain. Baltz made a number of projects on this subject, the best known of which, *The new Industrial Parks near Irvine, California,* was first published in 1974. With this book Baltz took his place near the center of the New Topographics movement, a newly coined term emblematic of a cool, distanced, yet critical view of the emerging man-altered landscape. The Topographic position, detached and glacial, has since influenced photographic practice in the United States, Germany and Japan.

A lot of people liked albums, family snapshots, but I never did. I liked the photographs in Real Estate office windows, which are technically correct and heartbreakingly empty. Lewis Baltz

Lewis Baltz
The new Industrial Parks
near Irvine, California

Book design by Lewis Baltz,
Gerhard Steidl and Bernard Fischer
96 pages
11 × 10.6 in. / 27.9 × 26.8 cm
51 black-and-white photographs
Quadratone
Clothbound hardcover with dust jacket

€ 58.00 / £ 54.00 / US$ 65.00
ISBN 978-3-86930-990-3

The new Industrial Parks
near Irvine, California

Das neue Industriegelände
in der Nähe von Irvine, Kalifornien

Lewis
BALTZ

Volume 1: Rainhill Hospital 1988-1990

Volume 2: Cammell Laird Shipyard 1993-1996

Tom Wood was born in County Mayo in
the west of Ireland in 1951. Initially
trained as a painter at the Leicester
Polytechnic, he has taken photographs
almost every day for the last 40 years.
His work has been shown in many solo and
group exhibitions including those at
Tate Britain, the Photographers' Gallery
in London and the International Center
for Photography in New York. Wood was
awarded the Prix Dialogue de l'Humanité
at Recontres d'Arles in 2002, and in 2014
he was the subject of the BBC documentary
What do artists do all day? Steidl has
published Wood's Photie Man (2005) and
Men and Women (2013).

Tom Wood
The DPA Work

Edited and book design by Tom Wood
and Cian Quayle
Texts by Cian Quayle, Audrey Linkman
and Clare Shaw
8.1 × 10 in. / 20.5 × 25.5 cm

Vol. 1: Rainhill Hospital 1988-1990
184 pages
10 black-and-white and 136 color
photographs

Vol. 2: Cammell Laird Shipyard 1993-1996
168 pages
42 black-and-white and 66 color
photographs

Vol. 3: Rainhill Archive Portraits
1890-1899
72 pages
68 black-and-white photographs

Four-color process
Three otabind softcovers in an
archival box

€ 80.00 / £ 70.00 / US$ 85.00
ISBN 978-3-95829-347-2

Beginning in 1985 the Manchester-based Documentary Photography
Archive (DPA) commissioned photographers to record aspects of
British society in the north of England. Tom Wood's *The DPA Work*
explores the life and demise of two major institutions near Liverpool,
Rainhill Psychiatric Hospital and Cammell Laird shipyard.

Opened in 1851 as a lunatic asylum for long-term patients, by
1936 Rainhill was the largest hospital complex in Europe. Wood began
photographing there in the 1980s when UK government policy had
shifted from institutions towards "Care in the Community." By then
Rainhill had diminished in size and wards were often combined, mixing
a range of patients. The DPA and the mental-health charity Mind,
which described conditions at Rainhill as "wholly unacceptable,"
asked Wood to record the hospital's closure and the movement of its
patients into the community.

Cammell Laird shipyard's illustrious history dates back to the
1820s, and includes the building of many famous warships and aircraft
carriers such as HMS Ark Royal. When Wood photographed the yard it
was facing closure, with a demoralized workforce fighting to save their
jobs while HMS Unicorn, the last Upholder-class submarine, was being
completed and launched.

The two main volumes of *The DPA Work* include archive material
related to the history of Rainhill and Cammell Laird, while a third book
features a series of late-nineteenth-century photographs of patients
at Rainhill. Together these volumes document a time of upheaval in
Liverpool in the midst of industrial decline, the breakdown of communities and changes in healthcare whose consequences are still felt
today.

Co-published with the University of Chester

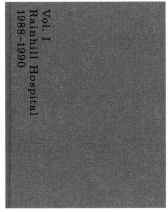

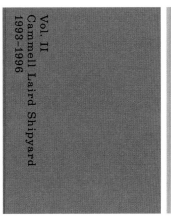

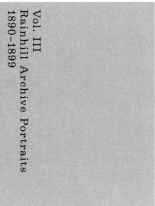

162

Born in Randfontein in 1930, David
Goldblatt is a definitive photographer of
his generation, esteemed for his engaged
depiction of life in South Africa over
more than 50 years. His work concerns
above all human values and is a unique
document of society during and after
apartheid. Goldblatt's photos are held
in major international collections, and
his solo exhibitions include those at the
Museum of Modern Art in New York in 1998
and the Fondation Henri Cartier-Bresson
in Paris in 2011. In 1989 Goldblatt
founded the Market Photo Workshop in
Johannesburg to teach visual literacy
and photography, especially to those
disadvantaged by apartheid. In 2006 he
received the Hasselblad Award and in
2016 was made Commandeur des Arts et
des Lettres by the French Ministry of
Culture. Goldblatt's books with Steidl
include On the Mines (2012), Particulars
(2014) and Ex-Offenders at the Scene of
Crime or Arrest (2017).

David Goldblatt
Fietas Fractured

Book design by Carla Saunders and David Goldblatt
256 pages
11.4 × 13 in. / 29 × 33 cm
90 black-and-white and 5 color photographs
Tritone and four-color process
Clothbound hardcover with a tipped-in photograph

€ 58.00 / £ 54.00 / US$ 65.00
ISBN 978-3-95829-325-0

This book presents photos by David Goldblatt taken between 1952
and 2016 of Fietas in Johannesburg, with an emphasis on his 1976–77
images of the suburb's last Indian residents before they were forcibly
removed under apartheid. Known affectionately by its inhabitants as
Fietas, though officially called Pageview, this was one of the city's few
"non-racial" suburbs, where Malay, African, Chinese, Indian and a few
white people lived. Composed of narrow streets and small houses
of two rooms and a kitchen for up to 15 people, here different races
and religions formed a strong, safe community where children played
in the streets. There were two mosques, Hindu, Tamil and Muslim
schools, cricket, soccer and bridge clubs, and 170 shops—customers
came from all over the Witwatersrand.

In 1948 the National Party came to power and made the clearance
of all "non-white" inhabitants of Pageview an immediate objective.
Some 5,000 Africans and other people of color were evicted or
"persuaded" to leave by the promise of better townships, while under
the Group Areas Act the Indians were to move to Lenasia, an apartheid creation 35 kilometers from the city. For 20 years the remaining
Indians fought against removal, principally in the courts, but in 1977
police and their dogs finally forced them out, except for a few. Almost
all buildings were destroyed and in their place new houses for lower-
income whites built. Today these are occupied by a mix of people
from Africa, Europe and Asia; no sense of community remains except
that of the homeless sheltering in the spaces left by demolition.

*I feel as though my teeth are being pulled out one by one. I run my
tongue over the spaces and try to remember the shape of what was
there.* Shop-owner Ozzie Docrat during the destruction of Fietas

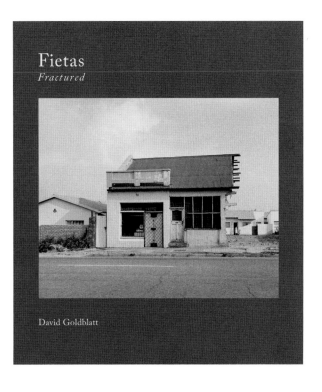

Born in Chicago in 1933, Bruce Davidson
began photographing at the age of ten in
Oak Park, Illinois. Davidson studied at
the Rochester Institute of Technology
and Yale University before being drafted
into the army. After leaving military
service in 1957, he freelanced for Life
and in 1958 became a member of Magnum
Photos. Davidson's solo exhibitions
include those at the Museum of Modern
Art, the Smithsonian American Art Museum
and the Walker Art Center, and his
awards include a Guggenheim Fellowship
and the first National Endowment for the
Arts Grant in Photography. In 2011 he was
awarded an honorary doctorate in Fine
Arts from the Corcoran College of Art
and Design. Davidson's books at Steidl
include Outside Inside (2010), Subway
(2011), Black & White (2012), England /
Scotland 1960 (2014) and Nature of Los
Angeles 2008-2013 (2015)

Lesser Known presents Bruce Davidson's photos made between 1955
and 1993 that have been overshadowed until now. Consisting of 130
images that have been consistently overlooked throughout Davidson's
long career, the book is the result of a year-long undertaking by the
photographer and his studio to examine 60 years of contact sheets
and edit individual images into a singular work that plots his professional and personal growth. *Lesser Known* showcases Davidson's
perpetual versatility and adaptability as a photographer through a
focus on early assignments, the intimate documentation of his family
life and smaller series such as unpublished color photographs from
major bodies of work including "East 100th Street" and "Campers."

This new body of work reflects both a passion and purpose over time.
Bruce Davidson

Bruce Davidson
Lesser Known

Edited by Teresa Kroemer, Meagan Connolly
and Bruce Davidson
Foreword by Bruce Davidson
Book design by Duncan Whyte
192 pages
9.4 × 12.6 in. / 24 × 32 cm
114 black-and-white and 16 color
photographs
Four-color process
Clothbound hardcover with
a tipped-in photograph

€ 58.00 / £ 55.00 / US$ 60.00
ISBN 978-3-95829-321-2

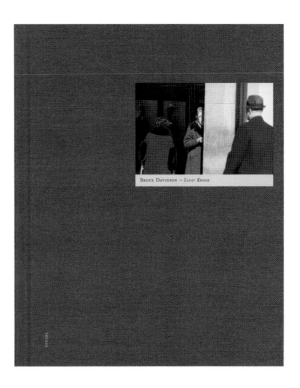

Born in 1946, Luke Powell holds degrees
in religion from the University of North
Carolina and Yale University. He first
visited Iran and Pakistan in the autumn
of 1971. During the Russian occupation
of Afghanistan his exhibition "The
Afghan Folio" traveled to 120 museums
and galleries, yet requests for further
exhibitions ceased when US intervention
began. From 2000 to 2003 Powell
photographed for the United Nations Mine
Action Centre for Afghanistan and other
UN agencies. Steidl published Powell's
Afghan Gold in 2013.

Luke Powell
Asia Highway

Text by Luke Powell
Book design by Luke Powell and Gerhard Steidl
232 pages
14.9 x 11 in. / 38 x 28 cm
203 color images
Four-color process
Clothbound hardcover with a tipped in photograph

€ 75.00 / £ 70.00 / US$ 85.00
ISBN 978-3-95829-327-4

Asia Highway is Luke Powell's photographic examination of Iran and
particularly Pakistan, acknowledging the destruction these cultures
have undergone while emphasizing the beautiful and good that Powell
discovered on his travels. The photos in the first chapter were taken
in Iran in 1974 and include the historical bazaar of Tabriz (a crucial
center on the Silk Road and since 2010 a UNESCO World Heritage
Site), while the succeeding chapters depict northern Pakistan. The
story of the book's origins orbits around various political events:
Powell photographed a series on Pakistan's Swat district after he had
left Afghanistan just ahead of the Taraki coup in 1978; and in 2000
the Taliban invited him to return while restricting his subsequent
movements, prompting Powell to travel to Pakistan and work in Chitral
and Gilgit. Other chapters explore Peshawar and the Kalash people in
Chitral.

*It is important to understand that people in Central and South Asia
have been literate for several millennia longer than in northern
Europe and North America. The simplicity of their lives and their
focus on families and children—these are not remnants of a primitive
past but survival-enhancing choices made by sophisticated people
who have seen civilizations rise and fall many many times before. A
relatively large percentage of the population lives in family-oriented,
agrarian and pastoral communities in which they can continue to
thrive after usury bubbles, trade routes and empires collapse, as they
always do.* Luke Powell

Asia Highway   Luke Powell

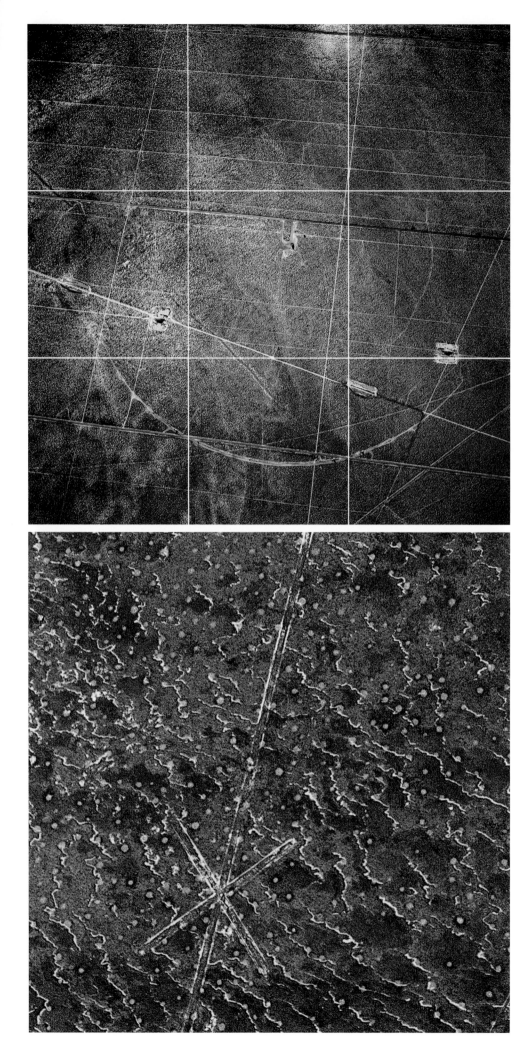

David Maisel
Proving Ground

Texts by Geoff Manaugh, William L. Fox
and Tyler Green
Book design by Aufuldish & Warinner
200 pages
11.5 x 11.5 in. / 29.2 x 29.2 cm
124 color images
Tritone and four-color process
Clothbound hardcover

€ 65.00 / £ 60.00 / US$ 70.00
ISBN 978-3-95829-288-8

An unsettling encounter with one of the most secretive of American
military zones, *Proving Ground* is David Maisel's photographic investigation of Dugway Proving Ground, a classified site covering nearly
800,000 acres in a remote region of Utah's Great Salt Lake Desert.
From its inception during World War II to the present day, Dugway's
primary mission has been to develop and test chemical and biological
weaponry and defense programs. After more than a decade of inquiry,
Maisel was granted rare access to photograph the terrain, testing
facilities and other aspects of this deliberately obscured region of the
American atlas.
Comprising aerial and on-site photos made at Dugway, this body
of work explores questions surrounding military power, national
security and land use, as well as the limits of technology and human
endeavor. Maisel's engagement with Dugway challenges the capacity of
photography as visual evidence; his subjects resist easy interpretation
and thus multiply strands of meaning. *Proving Ground* is a critical
response to the extraordinary formal and political aspects embedded
at Dugway, in Maisel's words a "hidden, walled-off, secret site that
offers the opportunity to reflect on who and what we are collectively,
as a society."

*There's a kind of romantic myth of the American West that much of
my work interrogates: the American West as pure, as sublime, as what
Robert Adams has termed "a landscape of mistakes." In the more
than 30 years that I have made aerial photographs of environmentally
transformed and transfigured sites throughout this region, none has
seemed to encapsulate the difficult and problematic realities of our
present day as much as Dugway Proving Ground.* David Maisel

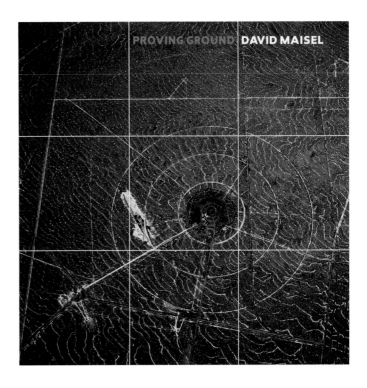

Backlist

Abbott, Berenice
The Unknown Berenice Abbott

€ 285.00 / £ 240.00 / US$ 350.00
ISBN 978-3-86930-650-6

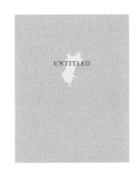
Adams, Bryan
Untitled

€ 125.00/ £ 95.00 / US$ 125.00
ISBN 978-3-86930-988-0

Abbott, Berenice
Paris Portraits 1925-1930

€ 68.00/ £ 58.00 / US$ 70.00
ISBN 978-3-86930-314-7

Adams, Bryan
Exposed

€ 68.00 / £ 60.00 / $ 75.00
ISBN 978-3-86930-500-4

A-chan
Off Beat

€ 20.00 / £ 16.00 / US$ 25.00
ISBN 978-3-86930-416-8

Adams, Robert
Gone?

€ 48.00 / £ 45.00 / US$ 55.00
ISBN 978-3-86521-917-6

A-chan
Vibrant Home

€ 20.00 / £ 16.00 / US$ 25.00
ISBN 978-3-86930-415-1

Adams, Robert
Tree Line

€ 35.00 / £ 30.00 / US$ 40.00
ISBN 978-3-86521-956-5

A-chan
Salt'n Vinegar

€ 40.00 / £ 35.00 / US$ 50.00
ISBN 978-3-86930-784-8

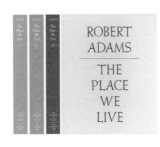
Adams, Robert
The Place We Live

€ 148.00 / £ 135.00 / US$ 175.00
ISBN 978-3-86930-533-2

Adams, Bryan
Wounded: The Legacy of War

€ 58.00 / £ 48.00 / US$ 65.00
ISBN 978-3-86930-677-3

Adams, Robert
The New West

€ 35.00 / £ 28.00 / $ 40.00
ISBN 978-3-86930-900-2

Bacigalupo, Martina
Gulu Real Art Studio

€ 38.00 / £ 30.00 / US$ 45.00
ISBN 978-3-86930-696-4

Bailey, David
NY JS DB 62

€ 45.00 / £ 40.00 / US$ 50.00
ISBN 978-3-86521-414-0

Badge, Peter
Nobel Heroes

€ 125,00 / $ 145,00 / £ 100,00
978-3-95829-192-8

Bailey, David
Pictures that Mark Can Do

€ 45.00 / £ 40.00 / US$ 50.00
ISBN 978-3-86521-367-9

Bailey, David
Bailey's East End

€ 98.00 / £ 85.00 / US$ 125.00
ISBN 978-3-86930-534-9

Bailey, David
8 Minutes

€ 45.00 / £ 40.00 / US$ 50.00
ISBN 978-3-86521-864-3

Bailey, David
Bailey's Democracy

€ 45.00 / £ 40.00 / US$ 50.00
ISBN 978-3-86521-192-7

Bailey, David
Flowers, Skulls, Contacts

€ 45.00 / £ 40.00 / US$ 50.00
ISBN 978-3-86930-128-0

Bailey, David
Havana

€ 45.00 / £ 40.00 / US$ 50.00
ISBN 978-3-86521-270-2

Bailey, David
Eye

€ 45.00 / £ 40.00 / US$ 50.00
ISBN 978-3-86521-708-0

Bailey, David
Is That So Kid

€ 45.00 / £ 40.00 / US$ 50.00
ISBN 978-3-86521-632-8

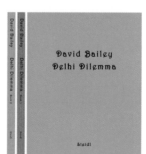

Bailey, David
Delhi Dilemma

€ 95.00 / £ 85.00 / US$ 115.00
ISBN 978-3-86521-991-6

Bailey, David
Tears and Tears

€ 45.00 / £ 40.00 / US$ 50.00
ISBN 978-3-86930-989-7

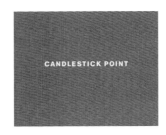

Baltz, Lewis
Candlestick Point

€ 65.00 / £ 58.00 / US$ 75.00
ISBN 978-3-86930-109-9

Balthus
The Last Studies

€ 480.00 / £ 440.00 / US$ 550.00
ISBN 978-3-86930-685-8

Baltz, Lewis
Venezia Maghera

€ 7,500.00 / £ 7,000.00 /
US$ 8,500.00
ISBN 978-3-86930-313-0

Baltz, Lewis
Works – Last Edition

€ 950.00 / £ 850.00 / US$ 1000.00
ISBN 978-3-95829-132-4

Baltz, Lewis
Lewis Baltz

€ 70.00 / £ 60.00 / $ 80.00
ISBN 978-3-95829-279-6

Baltz, Lewis
Rule Without Exception /
Only Exceptions

€ 65.00 / £ 50.00 / US$ 80.00
ISBN 978-3-86930-110-5

Banier, François-Marie
Imprudences

€ 38.00/ £ 32.00 / US$ 45.00
ISBN 978-3-86930-919-4

Baltz, Lewis
Common Objects

€ 40.00 / £ 30.00 / US$ 50.00
ISBN 978-3-86930-785-5

Banier, François-Marie
Never Stop Dancing

€ 10.00/ £ 8.00 / US$ 12.00
ISBN 978-3-86930-577-6

Baltz, Lewis
Texts

€ 24.00 / £ 20.00 / US$ 30.00
ISBN 978-3-86930-436-6

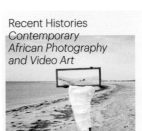

Baumann/Chuang/Onabanjo (eds.)
Recent Histories

€ 58,00 / $ 60,00 / £ 55,00
978-3-95829-350-2

Beuys, Joseph; Staeck, Klaus
Honey is flowing in all directions

€ 35.00 / £ 30.00 / US$ 40.00
ISBN 978-3-88243-538-2

Bolofo, Koto
Venus Williams

€ 45.00 / £ 35.00 / US$ 55.00
ISBN 978-3-86521-602-1

Blumenfeld, Erwin
Blumenfeld Studio

€ 34.00 / £ 28.00 / $ 40.00
ISBN 978-3-86930-531-8

Bolofo, Koto
Vroom! Vroom!

€ 45.00 / £ 35.00 / US$ 55.00
ISBN 978-3-86521-961-9

Billows, William /
Körber, Sebastian (eds.)
Global Game. Sport, Culture,
Development and Foreign Policy
Culture Report EUNIC Yearbook 2016

€ 15.00 / £ 12.00 / $ 20.00
ISBN 978-3-95829-198-0

Bolofo, Koto /
Van Ryssen-Bolofo, Claudia
The Prison

€ 45.00/ £ 35.00 / US$ 55.00
ISBN 978-3-86930-600-1

Bischoff, Jürgen /
Gerigk, Christoph (eds.)
Diving to the Pharaohs - Franck
Goddio's Discoveries in Egypt

€ 40.00 / £ 32.00 / $ 45.00
ISBN 978-3-95829-179-9

Bolofo, Koto
Rolls Royce

€ 45.00/ £ 35.00 / US$ 55.00
ISBN 978-3-86930-645-2

Bolofo, Koto
Große Komplikation /
Grand Complication

€ 98.00 / £ 89.00 / US$ 100.00
ISBN 978-3-86930-055-9

Bourdin, Guy
A Message For You

€ 55.00/ £ 50.00 / US$ 65.00
ISBN 978-3-86930-551-6

Bolofo, Koto
Lord Snowdon

€ 75.00 / £ 68.00 / US$ 85.00
ISBN 978-3-86930-329-1

Bourdin, Guy
Untouched

€ 55,00 / $ 65,00 / £ 50,00
978-3-86930-934-7

Brookman, Philip
Redlands

€ 28.00 / £ 24.00 / $ 34.00
ISBN 978-3-86930-686-5

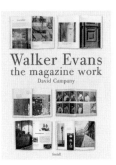

Campany, David (ed.)
Walker Evans: the magazine work

€ 48.00 / £ 40.00 / US$ 58.00
ISBN 978-3-86930-259-1

Burri, Rene
Movements

€ 85.00/ £ 75.00 / US$ 95.00
ISBN 978-3-86930-820-3

Cartier-Bresson, Henri
The Decisive Moment

€ 98.00 / £ 78.00 / US$ 125.00
ISBN 978-3-86930-788-6

Burtynsky, Edward
Oil

€ 98.00 / £ 85.00 / US$ 125.00
ISBN 978-3-86521-943-5

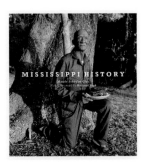

Clay, Maude Schuyler
Mississippi History

€ 65.00 / £ 58.00 / US$ 75.00
ISBN 978-3-86930-974-3

Burtynsky, Edward
Water

€ 98.00 / £ 85.00 / US$ 125.00
ISBN 978-3-86930-679-7

Clay, Langdon
Cars – New York City, 1974–1976

€ 85.00 / £ 78.00 / US$ 95.00
ISBN 978-3-95829-171-3

Burtynsky, Edward
Salt Pans
Little Rann of Kutch, Gujarat,
India

€ 58.00 / £ 50.00 / $ 60.00
ISBN 978-3-95829-240-6

Close, Chuck
Sribble Book: Self Portrait

€ 125.00 / £ 100.00 / US$ 145.00
ISBN 978-3-86521-492-8

Callahan, Harry
Seven Collages

€ 28.00 / £ 22.00 / US$ 40.00
ISBN 978-3-86930-140-2

Cohen, John
Here and Gone

€ 38.00 / £ 32.00 / US$ 48.00
ISBN 978-3-86930-604-9
–

Cohen, John
The High & Lonesome Sound

€ 45.00 / £ 35.00 / US$ 50.00
ISBN 978-3-86930-254-6

D'Agati, Mauro
Palermo Unsung

€ 45.00 / £ 39.50 / US$ 50.00
ISBN 978-3-86521-918-3

Cohen, John
Cheap rents … and de Kooning

€ 24.00 / £ 20.00 / US$ 25.00
ISBN 978-3-86930-903-3

D'Agati, Mauro
Marzia's Family

€ 40.00 / £ 34.00 / US$ 45.00
ISBN 978-3-86930-605-6

Cohen, John
Walking in the Light

€ 38.00 / £ 30.00 / US$ 45.00
ISBN 978-3-86930-772-5

d'Urso, Alessandra /
Borghese, Alessandra
For Friends

€ 95.00 / £ 80.00 / US$ 95.00
ISBN 978-3-95829-133-1

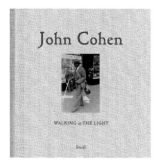

Comte, Michel
Light

€ 98,00 / $ 125,00 / £ 85,00
978-3-95829-119-5

d'Urso, Alessandra /
Borghese, Alessandra
Jubileum

978-3-95829-258-1
€ 28,00 / $ 30,00 / £ 25,00

D'Agati, Mauro
Alamar

€ 45.00 / £ 35.00 / US$ 50.00
ISBN 978-3-86521-954-1

Davidson, Anna Mia
Cuba: Black and White

€ 48.00 / £ 40.00 / $ 60.00
ISBN 978-3-95829-028-0

D'Agati, Mauro
Sit Lux et Lux Fuit

€ 48.00 / £ 38.00 / US$ 50.00
ISBN ISBN 978-3-86930-488-5

Davidson, Bruce
In Color

€ 78.00 / £ 68.00 / US$ 85.00
ISBN 978-3-86930-564-6

Davidson, Bruce
Subway

€ 58.00 / £ 52.00
ISBN 978-3-86930-294-2

Depardon, Raymond
Manhattan Out

€ 35.00 / £ 30.00 / US$ 40.00
ISBN 978-3-86521-704-2

Davidson, Bruce
Black & White

€ 240.00 / £ 220.00 / US$ 250.00
ISBN 978-3-86930-432-8

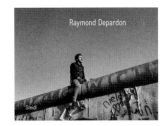

Depardon, Raymond
Berlin

€ 35.00 / £ 30.00 / $ 40.00
ISBN 978-3-86930-790-9

Davidson, Bruce
England / Scotland 1960

€ 38.00 / £ 30.00 / US$ 45.00
ISBN 978-3-86930-486-1

Diépois, Aline / Gizolme
Abstrakt Zermatt

€ 40.00 / £ 35.00 / US$ 45.00
ISBN 978-3-95829-580-6

Davidson, Bruce
Outside Inside

€ 240.00 / £ 220.00 / US$ 250.00
ISBN 978-3-86521-908-4

diCorcia, Philip-Lorca
Hustlers

€ 98.00 / £ 78.00 / US$ 125.00
ISBN 978-3-86930-617-9

Davidson, Bruce
Nature of Los Angeles

€ 38.00 / £ 30.00 / US$ 45.00
ISBN 978-3-86930-814-2

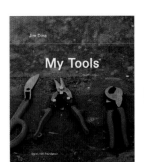

Dine, Jim
My Tools

€ 28.00 / £ 20.00 / US$ 35.00
ISBN 978-3-86930-828-9

Dean, Tacita
Seven Books Grey

€ 78.00 / £ 70.00 / US$ 95.00
ISBN 978-3-86930-299-7

Dine, Jim
A History of Communism

€ 15.00 / £ 12.00 / US$ 18.00
ISBN 978-3-86930-791-6

Dine, Jim
Donkey in the Sea before Us

€ 12.00 / £ 10.00 / US$ 14.95
ISBN 978-3-86930-451-9

Dine, Jim
Hello Yellow Glove

€ 28.00 / £ 20.00 / US$ 35.00
ISBN 978-3-86930-484-7

Dine, Jim
Birds

€ 50.00 / £ 35.00 / US$ 55.00
ISBN 978-3-88243-240-4

Dine, Jim
Printmaker's Document

€ 30.00 / £ 25.00 / US$ 40.00
ISBN 978-3-86930-644-5

Dine, Jim
Entrada Drive

€ 50.00 / £ 35.00 / US$ 55.00
ISBN 978-3-86521-080-7

Doisneau, Robert
From Craft to Art

€ 38.00 / £ 34.00 / US$ 50.00
ISBN 978-3-86930-025-2

Dine, Jim
The Photographs,
So Far (vols. 1-4)

€ 150.00 / £ 125.00 / US$ 180.00
ISBN 978-3-88243-905-2

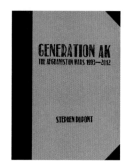

Dupont, Stephen
Generation AK

€ 78.00 / £ 70.00 / US$ 85.00
ISBN 978-3-86930-727-5

Dine, Jim
This Goofy Life of Constant
Mourning

€ 48.00 / £ 40.00 / US$ 55.00
ISBN 978-3-88243-967-0

Eggleston, William
From Black and White to Color

€ 38.00 / £ 32.00 / US$ 45.00
ISBN 978-3-86930-793-0

Dine, Jim
This Is How I Remember Now

€ 48.00 / £ 33.00 / US$ 50.00
ISBN 978-3-86521-603-8

Eggleston, William
Los Alamos

€ 248.00 / £ 220.00 / US$ 300.00
ISBN 978-3-86930-532-5

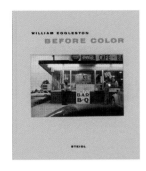

Eggleston, William
Before Color

€ 48.00 / £ 40.00 / US$ 55.00
ISBN 978-3-86930-122-8

Eggleston, William
At Zenith

€ 48.00 / £ 40.00 / US$ 55.00
ISBN 978-3-86930-710-7

Eggleston, William
The Democratic Forest

€ 550.00 / £ 420.00 / US$ 600.00
ISBN 978-3-86930-792-3

Eggleston, William
The Democratic Forest. Selected
Works

€ 45.00 / £ 38.00
ISBN 978-3-95829-256-7
[Distributed in the USA by David
Zwirner (D.A.P.)]

William Eggleston
Election Eve

€ 80,00 / $ 85,00 / £ 75,00
ISBN 978-3-95829-266-6

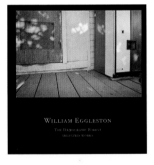

Elgort, Arthur
The Big Picture

€ 78.00 / £ 68.00 / US$ 85.00
ISBN 978-3-86930-543-1

Ehrlich, Richard
Face The Music

€ 50.00/ £ 45.00 / US$ 55.00
ISBN 978-3-86930-966-8

Epstein, Mitch
New York Arbor

€ 58.00 / £ 38.00 / US$ 68.00
ISBN 978-3-86930-581-3

Epstein, Mitch
Berlin

€ 45.00 / £ 40.00 / US$ 55.00
ISBN 978-3-86930-224-9

Epstein, Mitch
American Power

€ 65.00 / £ 60.00 / US$ 75.00
ISBN 978-3-86521-924-4

Eskildsen, Joakim
American Realities

€ 32.00/ £ 28.00 / US$ 40.00
ISBN 978-3-86930-734-3

Ewald, Wendy (et al)
The transformation of this world
depends on you

€ 24.00 / £ 18.00 / US$ 30.00
ISBN 9-783-86930-741-1

Faurer, Louis
Louis Faurer

€ 34.00 / £ 29,80 / $ 40.00
ISBN 978-3-95829-247-5

Frank, Robert
Frank Films

€ 45.00 / £ 40.00 / US$ 50.00
ISBN 978-3-86521-815-5

Fernandes, Walter
Angola Cinemas

€ 45.00 / £ 40.00 / $ 55.00
ISBN 978-3-86930-794-7

Frank, Henry
Father Photographer

€ 24.00 / £ 20.00 / US$ 25.00
ISBN 978-3-86521-814-8

Ferrez, Marc / Polidori, Robert
Rio

€ 125.00 / £ 80.00 / $ 100.00
ISBN 978-3-86930-910-1

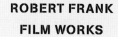

Frank, Robert
Film Works

€ 150.00 / £ 120.00 / US$ 175.00
ISBN 978-3-95829-036-5

Frank, Robert
The Americans

€ 35.00 / £ 30.00 / US$ 40.00
ISBN 978-3-86521-584-0

Frank, Robert
HOLD STILL–keep going

€ 40.00 / £ 30.00 / US$ 40.00
ISBN 978-3-86930-904-0

Frank, Robert
Looking In: Robert Frank's The
Americans – Expanded Edition

€ 85.00 / £ 75.00 / US$ 95.00
ISBN 978-3-86521-806-3

Frank, Robert
Household Inventory Record

€ 30.00 / £ 25.00 / US$ 35.00
ISBN 978-3-86930-660-5

Frank, Robert
Come Again

€ 35.00 / £ 30.00 / US$ 40.00
ISBN 978-3-86521-261-0

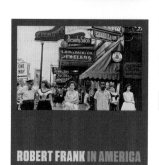

Frank, Robert
In America

€ 45.00 / £ 40.00 / US$ 50.00
ISBN 978-3-86930-735-0

Frank, Robert
Me and My Brother

€ 38.00 / £ 34.00 / US$ 45.00
ISBN 978-3-86521-363-1

Frank, Robert
Partida

€ 27.00 / £ 24.00 / US$ 30.00
ISBN 978-3-86930-795-4

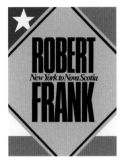

Frank, Robert
New York to Nova Scotia

€ 35.00 / £ 30.00 / US$ 45.00
ISBN 978-3-86521-013-5

Frank, Robert
Peru

€ 30.00 / £ 20.00 / US$ 35.00
ISBN 978-3-86521-692-2

Frank, Robert
One Hour

€ 10.00 / £ 10.00 / US$ 20.00
ISBN 978-3-86521-364-8

Frank, Robert
Pull My Daisy

€ 10.00 / £ 10.00 / US$ 20.00
ISBN 978-3-86521-673-1

Frank, Robert
Pangnirtung

€ 35.00 / £ 30.00 / US$ 40.00
ISBN 978-3-86930-198-3

Frank, Robert
Tal Uf Tal Ab

€ 27.00 / £ 24.00 / US$ 30.00
ISBN 978-3-86930-101-3

Frank, Robert
Paris

€ 35.00 / £ 30.00 / US$ 40.00
ISBN 978-3-86521-524-6

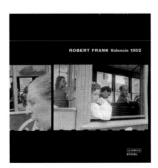

Frank, Robert
Valencia

€ 35.00 / £ 30.00 / US$ 40.00
ISBN 978-3-86930-502-8

Frank, Robert
Park/Sleep

€ 27.00 / £ 24.00 / US$ 30.00
ISBN 978-3-86930-585-1

Frank, Robert
Was haben wir gesehen /
What we have seen

€ 27.00 / £ 24.00 / US$ 30.00
ISBN 978-3-95829-095-2

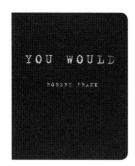

Frank, Robert
You Would

€ 27.00 / £ 24.00 / US$ 30.00
ISBN 978-3-86930-418-2

Frank, Robert
Zero Mostel Reads a Book

€ 15.00 / £ 10.00 / US$ 18.00
ISBN 978-3-86521-586-4

Frank, Robert
Leon of Juda

ISBN 978-3-95829-311-1
€ 27,00 / £ 24,00 / $ 30,00

Frank, Robert
Lines of My Hand

€ 30,00 / $ 35,00 / £ 28,00
ISBN 978-3-95829-320-5

Museum, Folkwang (ed.)
Dancing with Myself
Self-Portrait and Self-Invention:
Works from the Pinault Collection

€ 30.00 / £ 26.00 / $ 35.00
ISBN 978-3-95829-172-0

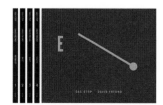

Freund, David
Gas Stop

€ 98.00 / £ 89.00 / $ 125.00
ISBN 978-3-95829-173-7

Friedlander, Lee
Chain Link

€ 38,00 / $ 40,00 / £ 34,00
ISBN 978-3-95829-259-8

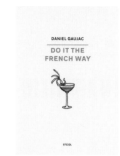

Daniel Gaujac
Do it the French Way

978-3-95829-270-3
€ 24,00 / $ 28,00 / £ 20,00

Gohlke, Frank / Sternfeld, Joel
Landscape as Longing: Queens,
New York

€ 65.00 / £ 55.00 / $ 75.00
ISBN 978-3-95829-032-7

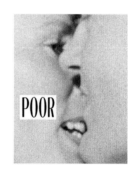

Goldberg, Jim
Rich and Poor

€ 75.00 / £ 65.00 / US$ 95.00
ISBN 978-3-86930-688-9

Goldblatt, David
In Boksburg

€ 45.00/ £ 38.00 / US$ 50.00
ISBN 978-3-86930-796-1

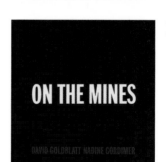

Goldblatt, David
On the Mines

€ 58.00 / £ 48.00 / US$ 65.00
ISBN 978-3-86930-491-5

Goldblatt, David
Particulars

€ 58.00 / £ 42.00 / US$ 70.00
ISBN 978-3-86930-777-0

Goldblatt, David
Regarding Intersections

€ 68.00 / £ 58.00 / US$ 75.00
ISBN 978-3-86930-714-5

Goldblatt, David
The Transported of Kwandebele

€ 65.00 / £ 48.00 / US$ 80.00
ISBN 978-3-86930-586-8

Goldin, Nan
Diving For Pearls

€ 35.00/ £ 30.00 / US$ 45.00
ISBN 978-3-95829-094-5

Goldin, Nan
A Beautiful Smile

978-3-95829-174-4
€ 35,00 / $ 40,00 / £ 30,00

Gonzalez-Torres, Felix

€ 58.00/ £ 48.00 / US$ 65.00
ISBN 978-3-86930-921-7

Gossage, John
The Thirty-Two Inch Ruler /
Map of Babylon

€ 58.00 / £ 52.00 / US$ 60.00
ISBN 978-3-86521-710-3

Grätz, Roland / Neubauer,
Hans-Joachim (eds.)
Human Rights Watch
Ed Kashi

€ 30.00 / £ 24.00 / $ 35.00
ISBN 978-3-95829-167-6

Graffenried, Michael von
Bierfest

€ 34.00 / £ 25.00 / US$ 40.00
ISBN 978-3-86930-680-3

Grant, Alexandra / Reeves, Keanu
Shadows

€ 48.00 / £ 42.00 / $ 60.00
ISBN 978-3-86930-827-2

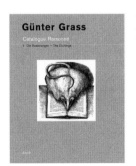

Grass, Günter
Günter Grass Catalogue Raisonné 1
The Etchings

€ 98.00 / £ 85.00 / US$ 98.00
ISBN 978-3-86521-565-9

Grass, Günter
Günter Grass Catalogue Raisonné 2
The Lithographs

€ 98.00 / £ 85.00 / US$ 98.00
ISBN 978-3-86521-566-6

Grauerholz, Angela
Angela Grauerholz

€ 58.00 / £ 48.00 / US$ 65.00
ISBN 978-3-95829-122-5

Gudzowaty, Tomasz
Beyond the Body

€ 38.00 / £ 32.00 / $ 45.00
ISBN 978-3-95829-040-2

Howard Greenberg Collection

€ 38.00 / £ 32.00 / US$ 45.00
ISBN 978-3-86930-736-7

Gudzowaty, Tomasz
Photography as a New Kind of Love
Poem

€ 78.00 / £ 65.00 / US$ 85.00
ISBN 978-3-95829-041-9

Greenberg, Howard / Shamis, Bob
(eds.)
James Karales

€ 58.00 / £ 45.00 / US$ 64.00
ISBN 978-3-86930-444-1

Gudzowaty, Tomasz
Closer

€ 88.00 / £ 78.00 / US$ 95.00
ISBN 978-3-95829-044-0

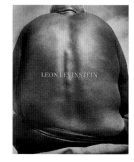

Greenberg, Howard / Shamis, Bob
(eds.)
Leon Levinstein

€ 68.00 / £ 58.00 / US$ 85.00
ISBN 978-3-86930-443-4

Gudzowaty, Tomasz
Proof

€ 30.00 / £ 25.00 / US$ 35.00
ISBN 978-3-95829-164-5

Grossman, Sid
The Life and Work of Sid Grossman

€ 48.00/ £ 45.00 / US$ 55.00
ISBN 978-3-95829-125-6

Gundlach, F.C.
The Photographic Work

€ 65.00 / £ 48.00 / US$ 75.00
ISBN 978-3-86521-594-9

Guirey, Kadir
L'album d'Eddy

€ 34.00 / £ 28.00 / US$ 45.00
ISBN 978-3-86930-548-6

Haas, Ernst
On Set

€ 58.00 / £ 48.00 / $ 70.00
ISBN 978-3-86930-587-5

Haas, Ernst
Color Correction

€ 48.00/ £ 40.00 / US$ 55.00
ISBN 978-3-95829-056-3

Horn, Roni
Another Water

€ 38.00 / £ 35.00 / US$ 45.00
ISBN 978-3-86930-318-5

Harlech, Amanda
Travelling in India

€ 32.00 / £ 25.00 / US$ 40.00
ISBN 978-3-86930-393-2

Horn, Roni
Haraldsdóttir, part two

€ 85.00 / £ 70.00 / US$ 95.00
ISBN 978-3-86930-317-8

Harris, Susan and Staniszewski,
Mary Anne (Eds.)
Exit Art

€ 50.00/ £ 40.00 / US$ 55.00
ISBN 978-3-86930-582-0

Horn, Roni
Cabinet of

€ 65.00 / £ 55.00 / US$ 75.00
ISBN 978-3-88243-864-2

Hechenblaikner, Lois
Winter Wonderland

€ 38.00 / £ 30.00 / US$ 40.00
ISBN 978-3-86930-284-3

Horn, Roni
Her, Her, Her, & Her

€ 35.00 / £ 24.00 / US$ 40.00
ISBN 978-3-86521-035-7

Hennek, Mat
Woodlands

€ 65.00 / £ 60.00 / US$ 75.00
ISBN 978-3-95829-178-2

Horn, Roni
Index Cixous

€ 22.50 / £ 15.00 / US$ 20.00
ISBN 978-3-86521-135-4

Hoppé, EO
The German Work

€ 58.00 / £ 48.00 / $ 65.00
ISBN 978-3-86930-937-8

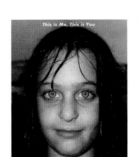

Horn, Roni
This is Me, This is You

€ 28.00 / £ 25.00 / US$ 30.00
ISBN 978-3-88243-798-0

Horn, Roni
bird

€ 40.00 / £ 34.00 / US$ 45.00
ISBN 978-3-86521-669-4

Horn, Roni
Th Rose Prblm

€ 38.00 / £ 32.00 / $ 40.00
ISBN 978-3-95829-271-0

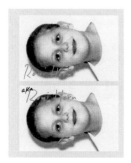

Horn, Roni
Roni Horn aka Roni Horn

€ 50.00 / £ 45.00 / US$ 60.00
ISBN 978-3-86521-831-5

Huyck / Katz
Views of Japan

€ 80.00 / £ 75.00 / $ 85.00
ISBN 978-3-95829-177-5

Horn, Roni
Herdubreid at Home

€ 20.00 / £ 13.00 / US$ 20.00
ISBN 978-3-86521-457-7

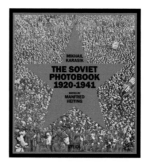

Karasik, Mikhail
The Soviet Photobook

€ 125.00 / £ 98.00 / US$ 150.00
ISBN 978-3-95829-031-0

Horn, Roni
AKA

€ 40.00 / £ 34.00 / US$ 45.00
ISBN 978-3-86930-133-4

Keel, Philipp
Splash

€ 48.00 / £ 38.00 / US$ 65.00
ISBN 978-3-86930-799-2

Horn, Roni
Hack Wit

€ 40.00 / £ 34.00 / US$ 45.00
ISBN 97-3-86930-982-8

Kia Henda, Kiluanji
Travelling to the Sun through the Night

€ 48.00 / £ 40.00 / $ 50.00
ISBN 978-3-86930-800-5

Horn, Roni
The Selected Gifts, 1974-2015

€ 40.00 / £ 34.00 / US$ 45.00
ISBN 978-3-95829-162-1

Killip, Chris
In Flagrante Two

€ 65.00 / £ 58.00 / US$ 75.00
ISBN 978-3-86930-960-6

Killip, Chris
Seacoal

€ 48.00 / £ 38.00 / US$ 60.00
ISBN 978-3-86930-256-0

Killip, Chris
Pirelli Work

€ 45.00 / £ 38.00 / US$ 50.00
ISBN 978-3-86930-961-3

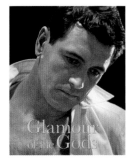

Killip, Chris
Isle of Man Revisited

€ 48.00 / £ 40.00 / US$ 60.00
ISBN 978-3-86930-959-0

Kobal Foundation (ed.)
Glamour of the Gods

€ 38.00 / £ 30.00 / US$ 45.00
ISBN 978-3-86521-682-3

Kuhn, Mona
Bordeaux Series

€ 58.00 / £ 50.00 / US$ 65.00
ISBN 978-3-86930-308-6

Kuhn, Mona
Evidence

€ 40.00 / £ 35.00 / US$ 45.00
ISBN 978-3-86521-372-3

Kuhn, Mona
Photographs

€ 40.00 / £ 35.00 / US$ 45.00
ISBN 978-3-86521-008-1

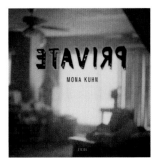

Kuhn, Mona
Private

€ 45.00 / £ 38.00 / US$ 60.00
ISBN 978-3-86930-709-1

Lagerfeld, Karl
Byzantine Fragments

€ 85.00 / £ 72.00 / US$ 110.00
ISBN 978-3-86930-246-1

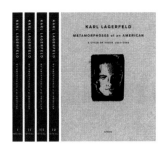

Lagerfeld, Karl
Metamorphoses of an American

€ 65.00 / £ 45.00 / US$ 85.00
ISBN 978-3-86521-522-2

Lagerfeld, Karl
Glory of Water

€ 88.00/ £ 75.00 / US$ 95.00
ISBN 978-3-86930-708-4

Lagerfeld, Karl
Casa Malaparte

€ 34.00 / £ 28.00 / US$ 40.00
ISBN 978-3-95829-033-4

Lagerfeld, Karl
Villa Noailles

€ 48.00 / £ 40.00 / US$ 60.00
ISBN 978-3-95829-037-2

Leiter, Saul
Early Color

€ 38.00 / £ 32,00 / US$ 45.00
ISBN 978-3-86521-139-2

Lagerfeld, Karl
Fendi by Karl Lagerfeld

€ 125.00 / £ 100.00 / US$ 145.00
ISBN 978-3-95829-034-1

Leutwyler, Henry
Ballet

€ 65.00 / £ 55.00 / US$ 75.00
ISBN 978-3-86930-906-4

Lagerfeld, Karl / Djian, Babeth
Numéro Couture by Karl Lagerfeld

€ 85.00 / £ 75.00 / US$ 95.00
ISBN 978-3-95829-057-0

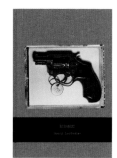

Leutwyler, Henry
Document

€ 65.00/ £ 58.00 / US$ 75.00
ISBN 978-3-86930-969-9

Leaf, June
Record 1974/75

€ 40.00 / £ 35.00 / US$ 45.00
ISBN 978-3-86930-045-0

The Photographs of Abraham Lincoln

€ 58.00 / £ 48.00 / US$ 55.00
ISBN 978-3-86930-917-0

Leaf, June
Thought is Infinite

€ 35.00 / £ 28.00 / US$ 40.00
ISBN 978-3-95829-102-7

Lifshitz, Sébastien
Amateur

€ 75.00/ £ 58.00 / US$ 90.00
ISBN 978-3-86930-739-8

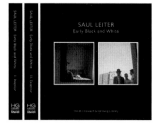

Leiter, Saul
Early Black and White

€ 68.00 / £ 58.00 / US$ 75.00
ISBN 978-3-86521-413-3

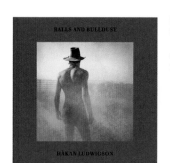

Ludwigson, Hakan
Balls and Bulldust

€ 68.00 / £ 58.00 / $ 80.00
ISBN 978-3-86930-707-7

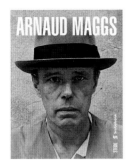

Maggs, Arnaud
Arnaud Maggs

€ 65.00 / £ 50.00 / US$ 80.00
ISBN 978-3-86930-591-2

Mocafico, Guido
Mocafico Numéro

€ 145.00 / £ 150.00 / $ 195.00
ISBN 978-3-86930-907-1

Maisel, David
Black Maps

€ 65.00 / £ 55.00 / US$ 85.00
ISBN 978-3-86930-537-0

Moffat, Curtis
Silver Society

€ 44.00/ £ 38.00 / US$ 50.00
ISBN 978-3-95829-027-3

Marchand, Yves / Meffre, Romain
Gunkanjima

€ 65.00 / £ 50.00 / US$ 85.00
ISBN 978-3-86930-546-2

Mofokeng, Santu
The Black Photo Album

€ 34.00 / £ 28.00 / US$ 50.00
ISBN 978-3-86930-310-9

Meer, Hans van der
European Fields

€ 38.00/ £ 32.00 / US$ 45.00
ISBN 978-3-86930-813-5

Mofokeng, Santu
Stories: 1, Train Church

€ 28.00 / £ 25.00 / US$ 35.00
ISBN 978-3-86930-971-2

Michener, Diana
Figure Studies

€ 28.00 / £ 24.00 / US$ 40.00
ISBN 978-3-86930-213-3

Mofokeng, Santu
Stories 2-4

€ 45.00 / £ 38.00 / US$ 55.00
ISBN 978-3-95829-104-1

Milella, Domingo

€ 58.00 / £ 48.00 / $ 55.00
ISBN 978-3-86930-487-8

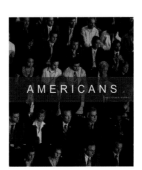

Morris, Christopher
Americans

€ 35.00 / £ 27.00 / US$ 40.00
ISBN 978-3-86930-448-9

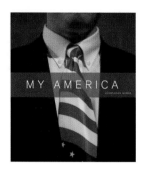

Morris, Christopher
My America

€ 35.00 / £ 27.00 / US$ 40.00
ISBN 978-3-86521-201-6

Muholi, Zanele
Faces and Phases 2006-14

€ 48.00 / £ 40.00 / US$ 65.00
ISBN 978-3-86930-807-4

Munkacsi, Martin
Martin Munkacsi

€ 65.00 / £ 58.00 / US$ 75.00
ISBN 978-3-86521-269-6

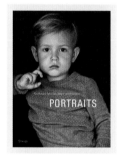

Müller-Westernhagen, Romney
Portraits

€ 42.00/ £ 35.00 / US$ 50.00
ISBN 978-3-86930-817-3

Nádas, Péter
Own Death

€ 40.00 / £ 28.00 / US$ 50.00
ISBN 978-3-86521-010-4

Neville, Mark
Fancy Pictures

€ 48.00/ £ 40.00 / US$ 55.00
ISBN 978-3-86930-908-8

Noguchi, Isamu
A Sculptor's World

€ 48.00 / £ 40.00 / US$ 60.00
ISBN 978-3-86930-915-6

Nozolino, Paulo
bone lonely

€ 34.00 / £ 32.00 / US$ 35.00
ISBN 978-3-86521-861-2

Nozolino, Paulo
Far Cry

€ 45.00 / £ 30.00 / US$ 50.00
ISBN 978-3-86521-122-4

Nozolino, Paulo
Makulatur

€ 24.00 / £ 21.00 / US$ 35.00
ISBN 978-3-86930-327-7

O'Neal, Hank
A Vision Shared
A Portrait of America 1935-1943

€ 68.00 / £ 60.00 / $ 75.00
ISBN 978-3-95829-151-2

Odermatt, Arnold
Karambolage

€ 65.00 / £ 55.00 / US$ 75.00
ISBN 978-3-88243-866-6

Odermatt, Arnold
On Duty

€ 65.00 / £ 55.00 / US$ 75.00
ISBN 978-3-86521-336-5

Odermatt, Arnold
Off Duty

€ 65.00 / £ 55.00 / US$ 75.00
ISBN 978-3-86521-796-7

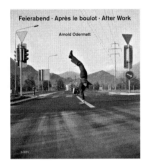

Odermatt, Arnold
After Work

€ 65.00 / £ 55.00 / US$ 75.00
ISBN 978-3-86930-973-6

Packham, Monte
Concentric Circles

€ 20.00 / £ 17.00 / US$ 27.50
ISBN 978-3-86930-024-5

Park Jongwoo
DMZ

978-3-95829-315-1
€ 35,00 / $ 40,00 / £ 30,00

Parke, Trent
The Christmas Tree Bucket,
Trent Parke's Family Album

€ 38.00 / £ 35.00 / US$ 45.00
ISBN 978-3-86930-206-5

Parke, Trent
Minutes to Midnight

€ 38.00 / £ 30.00 / US$ 45.00
ISBN 978-3-86930-205-8

Parks, Gordon
A Harlem Family 1967

€ 38.00 / £ 30.00 / US$ 45.00
ISBN 978-3-86930-602-5

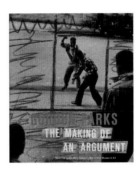

Parks, Gordon
The Making of an Argument

€ 38.00 / £ 30.00 / US$ 45.00
ISBN 978-3-86930-721-3

Parks, Gordon
Collected Works

€ 185.00 / £ 165.00 / US$ 225.00
ISBN 978-3-86930-530-1

Parks, Gordon
Collected Works – Study Edition

€ 125.00 / £ 115.00 / $ 145.00
ISBN 978-3-95829-262-8

Parks, Gordon
Back to Fort Scott

€ 38.00 / £ 30.00 / US$ 45.00
ISBN 978-3-86930-918-7

Parks, Gordon
I Am You

€ 35.00 / £ 38.00 / US$ 50.00
ISBN 978-3-95829-182-9

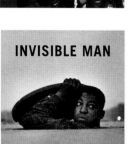

Parks, Gordon
Invisible Man

€ 38.00 / £ 30.00 / $ 45.00
ISBN 978-3-95829-109-6

Parks, Gordon
Segregation Story

€ 38.00 / £ 30.00 / $ 45.00
ISBN 978-3-86930-801-2

Parr, Martin (ed.)
The Protest Box

€ 225.00 / £ 185.00 / US$ 250.00
ISBN 978-3-86930-124-2

Paulsen, Susan
Wilmot

€ 48.00 / £ 35.00 / US$ 60.00
ISBN 978-3-86930-565-3

Paulsen, Susan
Sarah Ryhmes with Clara

€ 34.00 / £ 40.00 / US$ 50.00
ISBN 978-3-86930-244-7

Peterson, Mark
Political Theatre

€ 35.00 / £ 28.00 / US$ 40.00
ISBN 978-3-95829-183-6

Polidori, Robert
60 Feet Road

€ 98.00 / £ 88.00 / US$ 125.00
ISBN 978-3-95829-111-9

Polidori, Robert
After the Flood

€ 85.00 / £ 75.00 / US$ 95.00
ISBN 978-3-86521-277-1

Polidori, Robert
Parcours Muséologique Revisité

€ 125.00 / £ 100.00 / US$ 150.00
ISBN 978-3-86521-702-8

Polidori, Robert
Chronophagia

€ 48.00 / £ 40.00 / US$ 55.00
ISBN 978-3-86930-698-8

Polidori, Robert
Eye and I

€ 48.00 / £ 40.00 / US$ 65.00
ISBN 978-3-86930-592-9

Polidori, Robert
Hotel Petra

€ 48.00 / £ 42.00 / US$ 55.00
ISBN 978-3-95829-184-3

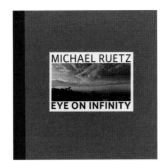

Ruetz, Michael
Eye on Infinity

€ 48.00 / £ 45.00 / US$ 55.00
ISBN 978-3-86521-766-0

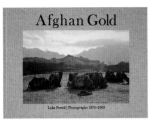

Powell, Luke
Afghan Gold

€ 98.00 / £ 95.00 / US$ 125.00
ISBN 978-3-86930-648-3

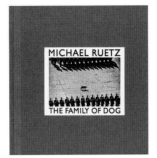

Ruetz, Michael
The Family of Dog

€ 38.00 / £ 30.00 / US$ 45.00
ISBN 978-3-86930-575-2

Provoke
Between Protest and Performance

€ 60.00 / £ 50.00 / $ 75.00
ISBN 978-3-95829-100-3

Ruetz, Michael
Eye on Time

€ 48.00 / £ 45.00 / US$ 55.00
ISBN 978-3-86521-577-2

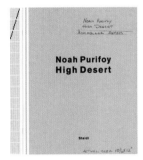

Purifoy, Noah
High Desert

€ 40.00 / £ 38.00 / US$ 60.00
ISBN 978-3-86930-595-0

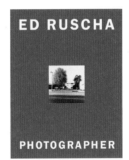

Rowell, Margit
Ed Ruscha, Photographer

€ 38.00 / £ 30.00 / US$ 45.00
ISBN 978-3-86521-206-1

Rautert, Timm
No Photographing (English)

€ 38.00 / £ 32.00 / US$ 45.00
ISBN 978-3-86930-322-2

Ruscha, Ed
THEN & NOW

€ 145.00 / £ 125.00 / US$ 185.00
ISBN 978-3-86521-105-7

Rautert, Timm
Josef Sudek, Prague 1967

€ 40.00 / £ 35.00 / US$ 50.00
ISBN 978-3-95829-118-8

Ruscha, Ed
Catalogue Raisonné of the
Paintings, Volume 1: 1958-1970

€ 165.00 / £ 145.00 / US$ 200.00
ISBN 978-3-88243-972-4

Ruscha, Ed
Catalogue Raisonné of the
Paintings, Volume 2: 1971-1982

€ 165.00 / £ 145.00 / US$ 200.00
ISBN 978-3-86521-138-5

Ruscha, Ed
Catalogue Raisonné of the
Paintings, Volume 3: 1983-1987

€ 165.00 / £ 145.00 / US$ 200.00
ISBN 978-3-86521-368-6

Ruscha, Ed
Catalogue Raisonné of the
Paintings, Volume 4: 1988-1992

€ 165.00 / £ 145.00 / US$ 200.00
ISBN 978-3-86521-833-9

Ruscha, Ed
Catalogue Raisonné of the
Paintings, Volume 5: 1993-1997

€ 165.00 / £ 145.00 / US$ 200.00
ISBN 978-3-86930-251-5

Ruscha, Ed
Catalogue Raisonné of the
Paintings, Volume 6: 1998-2003

€ 165.00 / £ 145.00 / US$ 200.00
ISBN 978-3-86930-740-4

Ruscha, Ed
Catalogue Raisonné of the
Paintings. Volume 7: 2004-2011

€ 165.00 / £ 145.00 / US$ 200.00
ISBN 978-3-95829-186-7

Ruscha, Ed
Los Angeles Apartments

€ 38.00/ £ 30.00 / US$ 45.00
ISBN 978-3-869630-596-7

Ryuichi / Heiting
The Japanese Photobook

€ 125,00 / $ 145,00 / £ 98,00
978-3-95829-176-8

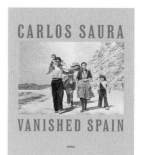

Saura, Carlos
Vanished Spain

€ 65.00 / £ 58.00 / $ 80.00
ISBN 978-3-86930-911-8

Mark Ruwedel

€ 48.00 / £ 38.00 / $ 65.00
ISBN 978-3-86930-928-6

Savulich, Andrew
The City

€ 38.00 / £ 30.00 / $ 45.00
ISBN 978-3-86930-690-2

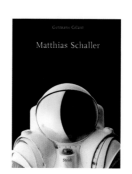

Matthias Schaller
ed. by Germano Celant

€ 65.00 / £ 58.00 / US$ 75.00

ISBN 978-3-86930-323-9

ISBN 978-3-95829-025-9(U.S.)

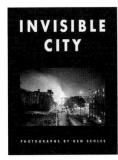

Schles, Ken
Invisible City

€ 34.00 / £ 28.00 /$ 40.00
ISBN 978-3-86930-691-9

Serra, Richard
Forged Steel

€ 38.00 / £ 32.00
ISBN 978-3-95829-188-1
[Distributed in the USA by David
Zwirner (D.A.P.)]

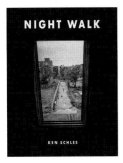

Schles, Ken
Night Walk

€ 38.00 / £ 30.00 /$ 45.00
ISBN 978-3-86930-692-6

Serra, Richard
Vertical and Horizontal Reversals

€ 58.00 / £ 52.00
ISBN 978-3-86930-978-1
[Distributed in the USA by David
Zwirner (D.A.P.)]

Schmidt, Jason
Artists II

€ 58.00 / £ 48.00 / US$ 70.00
ISBN 978-3-86930-632-2

Artists II

Richard Serra
Drawings

€ 75,00 / $ 80,00 / £ 62,00
978-3-95829-349-6

Schulze / Ruelfs (eds.)
ReVision

€ 48,00 / $ 58,00 / £ 45,00
978-3-95829-185-0

Swecz, Maria
inter esse

€ 38.00 / £ 30.00 / US$ 45.00
ISBN 978-3-86521-788-2

Serra, Richard
Notebooks, Vol. 1

€ 380.00 / £ 325.00 / US$ 400.00
ISBN 978-3-86930-253-9

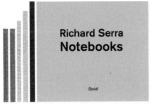

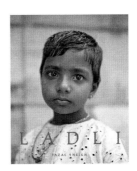

Sheikh, Fazal
Ladli

€ 35.00 / £ 30.00 / US$ 40.00
ISBN 978-3-86521-381-5

Serra, Richard
Early Work

€ 68.00/ £ 54.00 / US$ 85.00
ISBN 978-3-86930-716-9

Sheikh, Fazal
Portraits

€ 48.00 / £ 42.00 / US$ 55.00
ISBN 978-3-86521-819-3

Sheikh, Fazal
Moksha

€ 65.00 / £ 55.00 / US$ 70.00
ISBN 978-3-86521-125-5

Singh, Dayanita
Museum Bhavan

€ 75.00 / £ 68.00 / $ 85.00
ISBN 978-3-95829-161-4

Sheikh, Fazal
The Circle

€ 30.00 / £ 20.00 / US$ 40.00
ISBN 978-3-86521-599-4

Staeck, Klaus / Steidl, Gerhard
Beuys Book

€ 45.00 / £ 40.00 / US$ 50.00
ISBN 978-3-86521-914-5

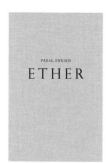

Sheikh, Fazal
Ether

€ 38.00 / £ 30.00 / US$ 45.00
ISBN 978-3-86930-653-7

Steidl-Werk No. 23
Masaho Anotani, Deformed

€ 48.00 / £ 40.00 / $ 55.00
ISBN 978-3-95829-120-1

Sheikh, Fazal
The Erasure Trilogy

€ 98.00 / £ 85.00 / US$ 125.00
ISBN 978-3-86930-805-0

Sternfeld, Joel
On This Site

€ 48.00 / £ 42.00 / US$ 55.00
ISBN 978-3-86930-434-2

Singh, Dayanita
Museum of Chance

€ 48.00 / £ 40.00 / US$ 55.00
ISBN 978-3-86930-693-3

Sternfeld, Joel
Walking the High Line

€ 28.00 / £ 25.00 / US$ 30.00
ISBN 978-3-86521-982-4

Singh, Dayanita
Dream Villa

€ 28.00 / £ 24.00 / US$ 35.00
ISBN 978-3-86521-985-5

Sternfeld, Joel
First Pictures

€ 48.00 / £ 42.00 / US$ 55.00
ISBN 978-3-86930-309-3

Sternfeld, Joel
iDubai

€ 28.00 / £ 24.00 / US$ 30.00
ISBN 978-3-86521-916-9

Sternfeld, Joel
When it Changed

€ 25.00 / £ 20.00 / US$ 30.00
ISBN 978-3-86521-278-8

Sternfeld, Joel
Stranger Passing

€ 65.00 / £ 50.00 / US$ 75.00
ISBN 978-3-86930-499-1

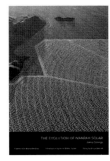

Stillings, Jamey
The Evolution of Ivanpah Solar

€ 65.00 / £ 58.00 / US$ 70.00
ISBN 978-3-86930-913-2

Sturges, Jock
Fanny

€ 78.00 / £ 65.00 / US$ 90.00
ISBN 978-3-86930-694-0

Subotzky, Mikhael / Waterhouse,
Patrick
Ponte City

€ 85.00 / £ 68.00 / US$ 100.00
ISBN 978-3-86930-750-3

Subotzky, Mikhael
Retinal Shift

€ 38.00 / £ 30.00 / US$ 45.00
ISBN 978-3-86930-539-4

Suzy Lake

€ 58.00 / £ 48.00 / $ 65.00
ISBN 978-3-95829-282-6

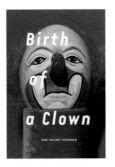

Taylor-Johnson, Sam
Birth of a Clown

€ 34.00 / £ 28.00 / US$ 40.00
ISBN 978-3-86521-853-7

Taylor-Johnson, Sam
Second Floor

€ 50.00 / £ 45.00 / US$ 60.00
ISBN 978-3-86930-264-5

Teller, Juergen
Nackig auf dem Fußballplatz

€ 25.00 / £ 18.00 / US$ 30.00
ISBN 978-3-88243-963-2

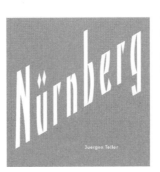

Teller, Juergen
Nürnberg

€ 75.00 / £ 65.00 / US$ 80.00
ISBN 978-3-86521-132-3

Teller, Juergen
The Keys to the House

€ 45.00 / £ 39.00 / US$ 50.00
ISBN 978-3-86930-383-3

Teller, Juergen
Märchenstüberl

€ 22.00 / £ 14.00 / US$ 30.00
ISBN 978-3-88243-863-5

Teller, Juergen
Woo!

€ 40.00 / £ 30.00 / US$ 45.00
ISBN 978-3-86930-652-0

Tese, Andrea
Inheritance

€ 35.00 / £ 28.00 / US$ 45.00
ISBN 978-3-86930-810-4

Teller, Juergen / Ghesquière,
Nicolas
I Just Arrived in Paris

€ 95.00 / £ 75.00 / US$ 125.00
ISBN 978-3-86930-823-4

Tillim, Guy
O Futuro Certo

€ 45.00 / £ 40.00 / US$ 50.00
ISBN 978-3-86930-649-0

Teller, Juergen / Ghesquiere,
Nicolas
The Flow

€ 24.00 / £ 20.00 / US$ 29.95
ISBN 978-3-86930-936-1

Trager, Philip
Photographing Ina

€ 38.00 / £ 34.00 / $ 45.00
ISBN 978-3-86930-977-4

Teller, Juergen / Ghesquiere,
Nicolas
Season Three

€ 24.00 / £ 20.00 / US$ 30.00
ISBN 978-3-95829-087-7

Trager, Philip
New York in the 1970s

€ 48.00 / £ 40.00 / $ 55.00
ISBN 978-3-86930-806-7

Teller, Juergen
Siegerflieger

€ 29.80 / £ 25.00 / US$ 35.00
ISBN 978-3-86930-914-9

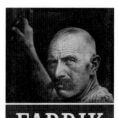

Tuggener, Jakob
Fabrik

€ 65.00 / £ 55.00 / US$ 75.00
ISBN 978-3-86521-493-5

Voit,Robert
New Trees

€ 58.00 / £ 45.00 / US$ 65.00
ISBN 978-3-86521-825-4

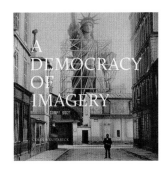

Westerbeck, Colin
A Democracy of Imagery

€ 45.00 / £ 40.00 / $ 50.00
ISBN 978-3-95829-116-4

Wallis, Brian (ed.)
The Order of Things

€ 85.00 / £ 78.00 / US$ 95.00
ISBN 978-3-86930-994-1

Wettre, Jonas
Once There were Polaroids

€ 30.00 / £ 25.00 / US$ 35.00
ISBN 978-3-86930-963-7

Weinberger, Karlheinz
Swiss Rebels

€ 65,00 / $ 68,00 / £ 58,00
978-3-95829-329-8

Wetzel, Gereon / Adolph, Jörg
How to Make a Book with Steidl

€ 15.00 / £ 12.00 / US$ 20.00
ISBN 978-3-86930-119-8

Wessel, Henry
Waikiki

€ 58.00 / £ 50.00 / US$ 65.00
ISBN 978-3-89630-300-0

Wiedenhöfer, Kai
Confrontier

€ 40.00 / £ 32.00 / US$ 45.00
ISBN 978-3-86930-550-9

Wessel, Henry
Incidents

€ 38.00 / £ 30.00 / US$ 45.00
ISBN 978-3-86930-697-1

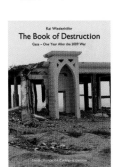

Wiedenhöfer, Kai
The Book of Destruction

€ 34.00 / £ 30.00 / US$ 40.00
ISBN 978-3-86930-207-2

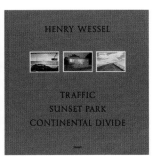

Wessel, Henry
Traffic. Sunset Park. Continental
Divide

€ 64.00 / £ 58.00 / $ 75.00
ISBN 978-3-95829-275-8

Wood, Tom
Men and Women

€ 68.00 / £ 58.00 / US$ 70.00
ISBN 978-3-86930-570-7

Whyte-Ball, Ken and Victoria (eds.)
The Golden Decade

€ 58.00 / £ 50.00 / $ 65.00
ISBN 978-3-86930-902-6

Zimmermann, Harf
Brand Wand

€ 78.00 / £ 65.00 / $ 90.00
ISBN 978-3-86930-628-5

Zander, Thomas (ed.)
Double Elephant 1973-74
Manuel Alvarez Bravo, Walker
Evans,Lee Friedlander, Garry
Winogrand

€ 98.00 / £ 85.00 / US$ 125.00
ISBN 978-3-86930-743-5

steidl.de